Math Bridge
5th grade

Written by:
Tracy Dankberg, Jennifer Moore & James Michael Orr

Project Directors: Michele D. Van Leeuwen
Scott G. Van Leeuwen

Creative & Marketing Director: George Starks

Design & Technical Project Director: Dante J. Orazzi

TABLE OF CONTENTS

INTRODUCTION

The *Math Bridge* series is designed to help students improve their mathematical skills in all areas. This book has been developed to provide fifth grade students with skill-based exercises in the following areas: place value, computation, estimation, number theory, time, money, data interpretation, measurement, capacity, geometry, decimals, fractions, and probability. The purpose of this book, therefore, is to strengthen students' mathematical concepts, thus helping them to become better mathematicians and to improve achievement test scores.

Math Bridge includes many extras to help your students in their study of mathematics. For instance,

✔ An Incentive Contract begins the book to motivate students to complete their work.

✔ A diagnostic test has been included to help assess your students' mathematical knowledge.

✔ Exercises become progressively more difficult as students work through the book.

✔ Tips are included throughout the book as reminders to help students successfully complete their work.

✔ Thought-provoking questions (Think About It) are periodically placed throughout the book to emphasize critical thinking skills.

✔ Additional exercises are included to help students in practicing with estimation.

✔ The exercises prepare students for standardized achievement tests.

✔ Each section includes problem-solving exercises written with the purpose of reinforcing the skills taught in that section.

Mathematics is all around us and is an essential part of life. It is the authors' intention that through the completion of this book, students will come away with a stronger knowledge of mathematics to assist them both inside and outside of the classroom.

Welcome to MATH FACTS

Math Facts, which are listed throughout the book, make mathematics more interesting by grounding it in world history, events, and science.

Incentive Contract

In • cen'tive, *n.* 1. Something that urges a person on. 2. Enticing. 3. Encouraging. 4. That which excites to action or moves the mind.

LIST YOUR AGREED-UPON INCENTIVE FOR EACH SECTION BELOW
Place a ✔ after each activity upon completion

Student Signature _____

PG	Activity Title	✔
9	Place Value	
10	Writing Numbers in Standard Form	
11	Reading Expanded Notation	
12	Changing the Place Value	
13	Finding New Quantities	
14	Problem Solving	

MY INCENTIVE IS ✖

15	Addition Strategies	
16	Adding With and Without Regrouping	
17	Comparing Sums	
18	Rounding & Estimating	
19	Problem Solving	

MY INCENTIVE IS ✖

20	Subtraction Strategies	
21	Subtraction Across Zeros	
22	Rounding & Estimating	
23	Problem Solving	

MY INCENTIVE IS ✖

24	Basic Facts	
25	Using Grouping Symbols	
26	Multiplying Two-Digit & Three Digit Numbers	
27	Multiplying Three-Digit Numbers with Tens	
28	Multiplying Larger Numbers	
29	More Practice	
30	More Practice	
31	Rounding to Estimate	
32	Estimation	
33	Problem Solving	
34	More Problem Solving	

MY INCENTIVE IS ✖

35	Basic Facts	
36	Using Grouping Symbols	
37	Dividing Three & Four-Digit Numbers	
38	Mixed Practice	
39	Problem Solving	
40	More Problem Solving	

MY INCENTIVE IS ✖

41	Finding Elapsed Time	
42	Estimating Time	
43	Problem Solving	

MY INCENTIVE IS ✖

44	Multiplying Money	
45	Dividing Money	
46	Problem Solving	

MY INCENTIVE IS ✖

47	Basic Figures	
48	Polygons	
49	Angles	
50	Triangles	
51	Circles	

Teacher or Parent Signature _____

52	Perimeter	
53	Area	
54	Problem Solving	

MY INCENTIVE IS ✖

55	Tenths & Hundredths	
56	Comparing & Ordering	
57	Rounding & Estimating	
58	Adding	
59	Subtracting	
60	Multiplying	
61	Dividing	
62	Problem Solving	

MY INCENTIVE IS ✖

63	Simplifying Fractions	
64	Fractions & Decimals	
65	Improper Fractions and Mixed Numbers	
66	Lowest Common Denominator	
67	Adding & Subtracting with Like Denominators	
68	Adding & Subtracting	
69	More Subtracting	
70	Multiplying Fractions	
71	Multiplying Mixed Numbers	
72	Problem Solving	

MY INCENTIVE IS ✖

73	Length in the Customary System	
74	Weight in the Customary System	
75	Capacity in the Customary System	
76	Problem Solving	
77	Metric System Length	
78	Metric System Weight	
79	Capacity in the Metric System	
80	Problem Solving	

MY INCENTIVE IS ✖

81	Ratios	
82	Equal Ratios	
83	Understanding Percent	
84	Percent of a Number	

MY INCENTIVE IS ✖

85	Outcomes	
86	Finding Probabilities	
87	Finding Averages	
88	Graphs	
89	Circle Graphs	

MY INCENTIVE IS ✖

DIAGNOSTIC TEST

Name _____ **Score** _____

Directions: Read the following problems. For each question, fill in the circle of the correct answer. If the correct answer is not given, fill in the answer space marked not given.

1. Which number is prime?
   - ○ A. 4
   - ○ B. 12
   - ○ C. 7
   - ○ D. 15

2. $28{,}346 + 84{,}237 = \square$.
   - ○ A. 211,344
   - ○ B. 121,307
   - ○ C. 112,583
   - ○ D. 125,483

3. Compare. $62{,}531 \bigcirc 506{,}213$
   - ○ A. <
   - ○ B. =
   - ○ C. >
   - ○ D. Not Given

4. $40 \div \square = 8$
   - ○ A. 2
   - ○ B. 4
   - ○ C. 5
   - ○ D. 10

5. Select the example whose product is even.
   - ○ A. $\begin{array}{r} 38 \\ \times\ 7 \\ \hline \end{array}$
   - ○ C. $\begin{array}{r} 39 \\ \times\ 7 \\ \hline \end{array}$
   - ○ B. $\begin{array}{r} 23 \\ \times\ 7 \\ \hline \end{array}$
   - ○ D. $\begin{array}{r} 81 \\ \times\ 5 \\ \hline \end{array}$

6. $(\square \times 4) + 8 = 16$
   - ○ A. 10 ○ B. 2 ○ C. 6 ○ D. 12

7. $90 \times 42 = n$
   - ○ A. 3,600
   - ○ B. 378
   - ○ C. 3,780
   - ○ D. 3,800

8. $725 \times 47 = n$
   - ○ A. 3,407
   - ○ B. 34,075
   - ○ C. 35,344
   - ○ D. 32,625

9. $\$7.68 \times 82 = n$
   - ○ A. $629.76
   - ○ B. $723.81
   - ○ C. $529.70
   - ○ D. $556.29

10. $360 \div 20 = n$
    - ○ A. 14 R2
    - ○ B. 15 R4
    - ○ C. 18
    - ○ D. 16

11. Find the average. 18, 17, 13, 12
    - ○ A. 14 ○ B. 15 ○ C. 12 ○ D. 16

Choose the best estimate.

12. $420 + 383 = \square$
    - ○ A. 900
    - ○ B. 1,000
    - ○ C. 800
    - ○ D. 8,000

13. $42 \times 38 = \square$
    - ○ A. 1,400
    - ○ B. 1,200
    - ○ C. 1,600
    - ○ D. 1,800

14. Choose the decimal for $9\frac{1}{2}$.
    - ○ A. 9.02
    - ○ B. 91.2
    - ○ C. 9.21
    - ○ D. 9.12

15. Which fraction is closest to $\frac{1}{2}$?
    - ○ A. $\frac{6}{14}$ ○ B. $\frac{2}{3}$ ○ C. $\frac{3}{4}$ ○ D. $\frac{1}{3}$

16. $31.75 + 43.58 =$
    - ○ A. 75.33
    - ○ B. 74.30
    - ○ C. 57.33
    - ○ D. 56.73

Name _____

17. What fraction is shaded?

○ A. $\frac{1}{4}$ ○ B. $\frac{1}{2}$ ○ C. $\frac{1}{3}$ ○ D. $\frac{2}{5}$

18. What is the whole or mixed number for $\frac{18}{4}$?

○ A. 3 ○ C. $4\frac{1}{2}$

○ B. $4\frac{1}{8}$ ○ D. $4\frac{4}{9}$

19. Compare $\frac{3}{8}$ ◯ $\frac{5}{9}$.

○ A. < ○ C. >

○ B. = ○ D. Not Given

20. $\frac{2}{5} + \frac{7}{10} = \square$

○ A. $2\frac{1}{5}$ ○ B. $\frac{9}{10}$ ○ C. $1\frac{1}{10}$ ○ D. 1

21. How many visitors were there in June?

Month	Visitors to Museum
April	◎◎◎
May	◎◎◎◎◎
June	◎◎◎◎◎◎

◎= 100 Visitors

○ A. 300 ○ C. 500

○ B. 400 ○ D. 600

22. Jennifer has 5 boxes. How many different ways can she arrange them in one row on her shelf.

○ A. 5 ○ C. 120

○ B. 20 ○ D. 80

23. What is the probability of the spinner stopping on 2?

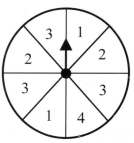

○ A. $\frac{1}{6}$ ○ B. $\frac{1}{4}$ ○ C. $\frac{1}{8}$ ○ D. $\frac{1}{5}$

24. A week ago, *Sam's Office Supplies* received 16 boxes of pens with 14 pens in each box. Today, they received 21 boxes of pens with 18 pens in each box. How many pens were received in all?

○ A. 580 ○ C. 520

○ B. 622 ○ D. 602

25. In a game, each contestant uses 3 tokens to move one space, 6 tokens to move 2 spaces, 9 tokens for 3 spaces, and 12 tokens for 4 spaces.   If the pattern continues, how many tokens does a player use to move 5 spaces?

○ A. 17 ○ B. 18 ○ C. 15 ○ D. 14

26. William bought 5 old American stamps for $3.20 and 6 foreign stamps for $2.50. How many stamps did he buy?

○ A. 4 ○ C. 11

○ B. 7 ○ D. 13

DIAGNOSTIC TEST

Name _____

27. In LaVista's Swimming Meet, Sue swam her lap in 125 seconds. Jane swam 18 seconds less than Sue. Melanie swam 20 seconds less than Jane. How many seconds did it take all 3 swimmers to finish?
- ○ A. 309
- ○ B. 319
- ○ C. 327
- ○ D. 412

28. Tracy's Hiking Club left for their hiking trip at 8:15 AM. They hiked at a rate of 2 miles per hour. If Rainbow Falls is 9 miles away, what time will they reach their destination?
- ○ A. 11:45 AM
- ○ B. 12:45 AM
- ○ C. 12:45 PM
- ○ D. 1:15 PM

29. What is the name of this polygon?

- ○ A. hexagon
- ○ B. octagon
- ○ C. quadrilateral
- ○ D. pentagon

30. Which figure is congruent to this polygon?

- ○ A.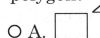
- ○ B.
- ○ C.
- ○ D.

31.
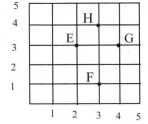
What point is named by (4, 3)?
○ A. E   ○ B. G   ○ C. H   ○ D. F

32.

Dan's Fresh Fruits	
Peaches	$3.50/bag
Oranges	$2.65/bag
Strawberries	$ .99/pt

Janet pays for 2 bags of oranges with $10.00. She receives 3 nickels, 2 quarters, and 4-one dollar bills. Which coin is needed to make correct change?
- ○ A. penny
- ○ B. nickel
- ○ C. dime
- ○ D. quarter

33. If it is 11:15 AM, what will be the time in 35 minutes?
- ○ A. 12:15 AM
- ○ B. 12:35 PM
- ○ C. 11:05 PM
- ○ D. 11:50 AM

34. 6 yd = _____ ft
- ○ A. 12   ○ B. 14   ○ C. 18   ○ D. 21

35. Name the space figure suggested by this object.
- ○ A. cylinder
- ○ B. cone
- ○ C. cube
- ○ D. sphere

36. 18 L = _____ mL
- ○ A. 1.8
- ○ B. 180
- ○ C. 1,800
- ○ D. 18,000

37. Seven degrees below zero Fahrenheit is the same as _____.
- ○ A. −70°F
- ○ B. −7°F
- ○ C. 7°F
- ○ D. 21°F

DIAGNOSTIC TEST

38. What is 433,765 rounded to the nearest hundred thousand?
    - ○ A. 300,000
    - ○ B. 340,000
    - ○ C. 400,000
    - ○ D. 430,000

39. Find x. $x - 14 = 27$
    - ○ A. 13 ○ B. 27 ○ C. 37 ○ D. 41

40. Find n. $n + 21 = 51$
    - ○ A. 36 ○ B. 30 ○ C. 18 ○ D. 24

41. $7,000 \times 60 = \square$
    - ○ A. 400,200
    - ○ B. 402,000
    - ○ C. 42,000
    - ○ D. 420,000

42. $1,480 \times 7 = \square$
    - ○ A. 13,600
    - ○ B. 10,360
    - ○ C. 10,300
    - ○ D. 16,000

43. What are two common multiples of 7 and 3?
    - ○ A. 14, 21
    - ○ B. 28, 24
    - ○ C. 21, 42
    - ○ D. 24, 36

44. $327.00
    $\times \quad 18$
    - ○ A. $588.60
    - ○ B. $5,886.00
    - ○ C. $5,680.60
    - ○ D. $5,580.60

45. $574 \div 4 = \square$
    - ○ A. 143 R2
    - ○ B. 133
    - ○ C. 114 R3
    - ○ D. 130

46. $2,536 \div 8 = \square$
    - ○ A. 307
    - ○ B. 317
    - ○ C. 273
    - ○ D. 373 R1

Choose the best estimate.

47. $7,080 - 4,702 = \square$
    - ○ A. 1,000
    - ○ B. 2,000
    - ○ C. 3,000
    - ○ D. 4,000

48. $370 \div 6 = \square$
    - ○ A. 600
    - ○ B. 60
    - ○ C. 70
    - ○ D. 50

49.

Movie Admission	
Adults	$6.00
Children	$3.00

Mrs. Moore and her 3 children went to a movie. How much did they pay?
- ○ A. $15.00
- ○ B. $13.00
- ○ C. $12.00
- ○ D. $ 9.00

50.

Refreshments Sales at Basketball Games

	Day 1	*Day 2*	*Day 3*
Popcorn	$133	$144	$160
Sodas	$175	$162	$123

How much more money in all was taken in on Day 1 than on Day 2?
- ○ A. $4
- ○ B. $2
- ○ C. $8
- ○ D. $6

STOP.

Whole Numbers: Place Value

Name _____

Write the value of each underlined digit. Study the chart below.
The underlined digit 6 is in the hundred thousands place. So it has a place value of 600,000.

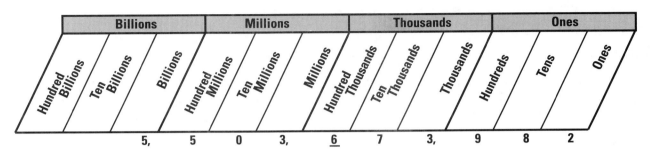

	Billions			Millions			Thousands			Ones		
Hundred Billions	Ten Billions	Billions	Hundred Millions	Ten Millions	Millions	Hundred Thousands	Ten Thousands	Thousands	Hundreds	Tens	Ones
	5,	5	0	3,	6	7	3,	9	8	2

1. 2,8<u>4</u>3

_____

2. 5,<u>7</u>01

_____

3. 62,<u>4</u>83

_____

4. 13,90<u>5</u>

_____

5. 3,<u>8</u>73,452

_____

6. 4<u>7</u>3,206,311

_____

7. 7<u>9</u>,337

_____

8. <u>6</u>38,317

_____

9. <u>7</u>,741,412

_____

10. 878,<u>3</u>04

_____

11. 7<u>4</u>8,244,862

_____

12. 98,4<u>2</u>3,648

_____

13. 458,2<u>3</u>1

_____

14. <u>9</u>81,324,109

_____

15. <u>1</u>,346,225

_____

 THINK ABOUT IT!

16. Write two 12-digit numbers so that one is exactly ten billion more than the other.

MATH FACTS
Math is the only universal language on earth! Numbers are the language of Math, not words like English, French, or Spanish! No matter where you live—the United States, Japan or Italy—you use the same basic math principles to add up the cost of a pizza, soda and candy.

Whole Numbers: Writing Numbers in Standard Form

Write each number in standard form.

      sixteen thousand, two hundred forty-three   <u>16,243</u>

    TIP: *Don't forget to use a comma to separate each group of three digits.*

1. eight thousand, five hundred sixty   _____

2. fifty-three thousand, twenty-four   _____

3. nine million, sixty-four thousand, seven hundred one   _____

4. sixteen million, eight hundred ninety-four   _____

5. thirty-six thousand, two hundred seventy-five   _____

6. five hundred six million, three thousand, two hundred   _____

7. seventeen billion, fifty-six million, three hundred forty-one   _____
   thousand, eighteen

8. twenty-eight million, five hundred sixty-one thousand,   _____
   one hundred twenty-two

9. seventy billion, eight hundred sixteen million, four hundred   _____
   twenty-one thousand, six

10. four hundred thirteen billion, seven hundred thirty-seven   _____
    million, sixteen

11. nine hundred fifteen billion, three hundred sixty-one million,   _____
    eight hundred twenty-four thousand, one hundred ninety-seven

12. five million, eight thousand, sixty-seven   _____

13. twenty-eight million, six hundred two thousand, one hundred   _____
    forty-three

14. forty-one billion, three hundred sixty-two million, one thousand,_____
    sixty-six

15. one hundred million, five hundred eighty-nine thousand, seven   _____
    hundred thirty-four

Whole Numbers: Reading Expanded Notation

Select the standard form of the numbers written in expanded notation.
Use the space to the right of the problem to find the answer.

$$9,000,000 + 800,000 + 3,000 + 100 + 90 + 2 =$$

$$
\begin{array}{r}
9,000,000 \\
800,000 \\
3,000 \\
100 \\
90 \\
+ \quad 2 \\
\hline
9,803,192
\end{array}
$$

TIP: *Always align the place values to find the number.*

---

1. $7,000,000 + 100,000 + 8,000 + 300 + 20$
    - ○ A. 718,032
    - ○ B. 7,018,032
    - ○ C. 7,108,320
    - ○ D. 71,832

2. $900,000 + 40,000 + 5,000 + 200 + 10$
    - ○ A. 9,405,210
    - ○ B. 945,210
    - ○ C. 904,510
    - ○ D. 945,201

3. $1,000,000,000 + 200,000,000 + 10,000,000 + 5,000,000 + 70,000 + 700 + 8$
    - ○ A. 1,215,070,708
    - ○ B. 1,215,070,780
    - ○ C. 1,201,537,708
    - ○ D. 1,210,537,708

4. $5,000,000 + 70,000 + 3,000 + 200 + 4$
    - ○ A. 57,324
    - ○ B. 5,073,024
    - ○ C. 5,073,204
    - ○ D. 5,703,024

5. $600,000 + 50,000 + 1,000 + 800 + 20$
    - ○ A. 65,182
    - ○ B. 651,820
    - ○ C. 605,182
    - ○ D. 650,182

6. $7,000,000,000 + 500,000,000 + 60,000,000 + 3,000,000 + 1,000 + 200 + 50$
    - ○ A. 7,500,631,250
    - ○ B. 7,563,001,250
    - ○ C. 7,056,312,050
    - ○ D. 7,005,631,250

7. $3,000,000 + 900 + 80 + 6$
    - ○ A. 3,986
    - ○ B. 3,009,806
    - ○ C. 3,000,986
    - ○ D. 39,086

Whole Numbers: Changing the Place Value

For each of the following, change one of the digits and give the amount the number changed.

*Change the 8 in 48,233 to 6. The new number is **46,233**.*
Therefore, it was decreased by 2,000.

---

1. Change the 5 in 25,136 to 7. How much higher is the new number?
   - ○ A. 7
   - ○ B. 2,000
   - ○ C. 2
   - ○ D. 7,000

2. Change the 3 in 173,286 to 5. How much higher is the new number?
   - ○ A. 200
   - ○ B. 20
   - ○ C. 2,000
   - ○ D. 2

3. Change the 6 in 4,358,617 to 2. How much lower is the new number?
   - ○ A. 40
   - ○ B. 400
   - ○ C. 4
   - ○ D. 2

4. Change the 2 in 207,314 to 8. How much higher is the new number?
   - ○ A. 8,000
   - ○ B. 6,000
   - ○ C. 800,000
   - ○ D. 600,000

5. Change the 4 in 6,040,328 to 9. How much higher is the new number?
   - ○ A. 5,000,000
   - ○ B. 90
   - ○ C. 500
   - ○ D. 50,000

6. Change the 7 in 37,951,086 to 8. How much higher is the new number?
   - ○ A. 100,000
   - ○ B. 1
   - ○ C. 1,000,000
   - ○ D. 8,000,000

7. Change the 8 in 28,496 to 3. How much lower is the new number?
   - ○ A. 5
   - ○ B. 5,000
   - ○ C. 8
   - ○ D. 3,000

8. Change the 2 in 6,200,436 to a 5. How much higher is the new number?
   - ○ A. 3
   - ○ B. 300,000
   - ○ C. 200,000
   - ○ D. 5,00,000

9. Change the 8 in 87,362 to 3. How much lower is the new number?
   - ○ A. 5,000,000
   - ○ B. 3
   - ○ C. 5
   - ○ D. 50,000

10. Change the 6 in 860,429 to 1. How much lower is the new number?
    - ○ A. 5
    - ○ B. 60,000
    - ○ C. 50,000
    - ○ D. 1

11. Change the 5 in 873,295 to 3. How much lower is the new number?
    - ○ A. 2
    - ○ B. 30,000
    - ○ C. 20,000
    - ○ D. 5

12. Change the 7 in 47,625 to 8. How much higher is the new number?
    - ○ A. 8,000
    - ○ B. 1
    - ○ C. 1,000
    - ○ D. 70,000

Whole Numbers: Finding New Quantities   Name _____

Increase or decrease each number by the given amount to find a new quantity.

*Increase the number 12,325 by **2,500;** the new quantity is **14,825.***

TIP: *Pay close attention to the place value that is being changed.*

1. Increase 312,486 by 400:
   - O A. 312,086
   - O B. 312,886
   - O C. 316,486
   - O D. 312,526

2. Increase 75,049 by 2,000:
   - O A. 77,049
   - O B. 73,049
   - O C. 77,049
   - O D. 75,249

3. Increase 2,416,573 by 6,000:
   - O A. 2,476,573
   - O B. 32,076,573
   - O C. 2,216,573
   - O D. 2,422,573

4. Increase 39,800 by 3,000:
   - O A. 36,800
   - O B. 39,500
   - O C. 42,800
   - O D. 40,200

5. Increase 75,146,921 by 2,500:
   - O A. 75,148,921
   - O B. 75,149,421
   - O C. 75,144,421
   - O D. 75,144,921

6. Decrease 137,506 by 75:
   - O A. 137,581
   - O B. 137,576
   - O C. 137,431
   - O D. 137,756

7. Decrease 2,364,137 by 1,200:
   - O A. 2,363,037
   - O B. 2,366,237
   - O C. 2,365,137
   - O D. 2,362,937

8. Decrease 699 by 60:
   - O A. 759
   - O B. 639
   - O C. 1,299
   - O D. 6,960

9. Decrease 7,000 by 500:
   - O A. 7,500
   - O B. 6,500
   - O C. 5,600
   - O D. 5,500

10. Decrease 438,294 by 1,500:
    - O A. 439,794
    - O B. 438,794
    - O C. 436,794
    - O D. 430,294

11. Increase 7,478 by 1,150:
    - O A. 1,578
    - O B. 1,528
    - O C. 1,778
    - O D. 1,428

12. Decrease 71,634 by 9,000:
    - O A. 79,634
    - O B. 62,634
    - O C. 80,634
    - O D. 72,534

13. Increase 8,621,498 by 30,000:
    - O A. 8,631,498
    - O B. 56,214,981
    - O C. 8,651,498
    - O D. 8,921,498

14. Increase 684,329 by 100:
    - O A. 684,429
    - O B. 685,329
    - O C. 684,229
    - O D. 683,329

15. Decrease 965,651 by 6,000:
    - O A. 960,651
    - O B. 959,651
    - O C. 905,651
    - O D. 965,051

16. Increase 295,687 by 20,000:
    - O A. 297,687
    - O B. 305,687
    - O C. 315,687
    - O D. 320,687

Whole Numbers: Problem Solving

Name _____

Solve each problem.

1. Write the number that has a 9 in the hundred thousand place, a two in the thousand place, a 5 in the hundreds place, and a 1 in the ones place.

   1. _____

2. What 4 digit number has a 5 in the ones place, a 7 in the hundreds place, a 9 in the thousands place, and 2 in the tens place?

   2. _____

3. The neighborhood park is one acre, or forty-three thousand, five hundred sixty square feet. Write the number describing an acre in standard form.

   3. _____

4. In the school yard, the flagpole stands 384 inches tall. Write the number in expanded form.

   4. _____

5. Tanner's family drove six hundred, forty-eight miles on a trip to the beach and seven hundred twenty miles on a trip to their grandparent's house. How many miles did the two trips take?

   5. _____

6. Monica needs 2,568 stamps to complete her collection. She already has 8,794. When her collection is complete, how many stamps will she have?

   6. _____

7. Garden Lake Elementary collected 35,821 cans in April for recycling. In May they collected 46,399. How many cans did they recycle those two months.

   7. _____

Addition: Addition Strategies

Name _____

Find each sum. Use mental math whenever possible.

1. $7 + 5 = \boxed{}$ 2. $16 + 7 = \boxed{}$ 3. $28 + 14 = \boxed{}$

4. $17 + 9 = \boxed{}$ 5. $18 + 29 = \boxed{}$ 6. $11 + 38 = \boxed{}$

7. $6 + 14 = \boxed{}$ 8. $19 + 15 = \boxed{}$ 9. $25 + 48 = \boxed{}$

10. $\begin{array}{r} 14 \\ 16 \\ +\ 9 \\ \hline \end{array}$ 11. $\begin{array}{r} 16 \\ 15 \\ +\ 7 \\ \hline \end{array}$ 12. $\begin{array}{r} 21 \\ 13 \\ +9 \\ \hline \end{array}$ 13. $\begin{array}{r} 25 \\ 39 \\ +16 \\ \hline \end{array}$ 14. $\begin{array}{r} 37 \\ 21 \\ +18 \\ \hline \end{array}$

15. $7 + 13 + 28 = \boxed{}$ 16. $(30 + 5) + 19 = \boxed{}$

17. $(15 + 9) + (15 + 4) = \boxed{}$ 18. $(16 + 8) + (12 + 6) = \boxed{}$

19. $27 + 9 + 4 = \boxed{}$ 20. $17 + (19 + 28) = \boxed{}$

21. $17 + (6 + 42) = \boxed{}$ 22. $20 + (45 + 35) = \boxed{}$

23. $25 + (25 + 25) = \boxed{}$ 24. $(22 + 12) + (18 + 30) = \boxed{}$

25. $49 + 1 + 50 = \boxed{}$ 26. $(19 + 15) + (12 + 12) = \boxed{}$

27. $(26 + 20) + 10 = \boxed{}$ 28. $(38 + 40) + (30 + 48) = \boxed{}$

29. $15 + 30 + 45 = \boxed{}$ 30. $(18 + 16) + (15 + 14) = \boxed{}$

31. $(44 + 30) + (19 + 6) = \boxed{}$ 32. $(13 + 23) + (6 + 12) = \boxed{}$

33. $(17 + 15) + (13 + 26) = \boxed{}$ 34. $(22 + 0) + (22 + 0) = \boxed{}$

35. $(15 + 15) + 18 = \boxed{}$ 36. $(12 + 18) + (16 + 14) = \boxed{}$

Addition: Adding With and Without Regrouping

Add.

1. 46
   + 9

2. 624
   + 19

3. 454
   + 29

4. 293
   + 46

5. 746
   + 89

6. 597
   + 46

7. 793
   + 68

8. 864
   + 96

9. 641
   +39

10. 863
    + 82

11. 966
    + 95

12. 2,364
    +   52

13. 7,468
    +   38

14. 6,384
    + 236

15. 5,234
    + 349

16. 8,624
    + 531

17. 16,436
    +   238

18. 27,946
    +   498

19. 35,076
    +   439

20. 430,972
    +   1,276

21. 575,138
    +   2,388

22. 732,144
    + 28,964

23. 2,364,295
    + 133,241

24. 6,487,325
    +1,328,194

25. 234,168,291
    + 1,349,276

26. 7,532,138
    + 1,123,345

27. 3,743,281
    + 364,245

28. 8,325,741
    +2,461,326

Addition: Comparing Sums

Compute each sum; then compare using >, <, or =.

$$7 + 12 \bigcirc 11 + 9$$
$$19 \quad < \quad 20$$

---

1. $13 + 9 \bigcirc 28 + 2$

2. $9 + 18 \bigcirc 36$

3. $18 + 4 \bigcirc 25$

4. $27 \bigcirc 19 + 13$

5. $29 \bigcirc 13 + 6$

6. $25 + 8 \bigcirc 38$

7. $48 + 12 \bigcirc 20 + 30$

8. $5 + (9 + 19) \bigcirc 43$

9. $17 + (5 + 29) \bigcirc 62$

10. $19 + (13 + 12) \bigcirc 22 + 18$

11. $23 + 14 \bigcirc 15 + 22$

12. $26 + 13 \bigcirc 9 + 18$

13. $(9 + 12) + 19 \bigcirc 23 + 15$

14. $(17 + 23) + 2 \bigcirc 9 + 36$

15. $17 + 20 \bigcirc 18 + 18$

16. $23 + (9 + 18) \bigcirc 42 + 18$

17. $19 + 6 \bigcirc 10 + 15$

18. $(17 + 9) \bigcirc (28 + 2)$

19. $(18 + 12) + 19 \bigcirc (0 + 24) + 24$

20. $(37 + 0) + 18 \bigcirc (9 + 16) + 45$

Addition: Rounding & Estimating

Name _____

Part I: Round each number to the greatest place value position.

3,852   rounds to 4,000

Look to the right of 3. If that number is 5 or greater, round up. If not, keep the number the same, and change all numbers to the right to zeros.

---

1.   47   _____

2.   93   _____

3.   78   _____

4.   53   _____

5.   356   _____

6.   923   _____

7.   6,551   _____

8.   31,254   _____

9.   853,572   _____

10.   322,374   _____

11.   702,874   _____

12. 5,893,139   _____

Part II: Round; then estimate the sum.

13.   74
     + 87

14.   46
     + 39

15.   83
     + 78

16.   65
     + 28

17.   246
     + 96

18.   878
     + 423

19.   625
     + 378

20.   3,824
     + 1,962

21.   73,284
     + 64,320

22.   80,720
     + 74,325

23.   2,396,841
     + 1,732,498

24.   4,562,033
     + 7,426,378

Addition: Problem Solving

Name _____

Solve each problem.

1. Kelly ran 45 miles the first month, 26 miles the second month, and 39 miles the third month. How many miles did she run in all?

2. At Saturday's game, the snack bar sold 235 bags of popcorn, 138 candy items, 75 pretzels, and 305 sodas. How many food items were sold in all?

3. Diana decorated 432 cardboard picture frames. She cut out 385 more frames to begin decorating next. If she finishes all of them, how many decorated frames will she have?

4. Melanie sold 372 raffle tickets for the school band. She needs to sell another 538 to reach the first place prize. How many in all does she need to sell to win the first place prize?

5. Elizabeth and her mother picked 320 strawberries on Monday, 564 on Tuesday, and 683 on Wednesday. How many strawberries did they pick over the three days?

6. Sam played in his school's basketball game on Saturday. He scored 28 points in the first two quarters. In the second half, he scored half of the team's 84 points. How many points did Sam score in Saturday's game?

1.

2.

3.

4.

5.

6.

Subtraction: Subtraction Strategies

Name _____

Subtract.

1. $11 - 6 =$ ☐

2. $13 - 6 =$ ☐

3. $16 - 4 =$ ☐

4. $12 - 8 =$ ☐

5. $15 - 6 =$ ☐

6. $15 - 9 =$ ☐

7. $17 - 9 =$ ☐

8. $21 - 8 =$ ☐

9. $18 - 7 =$ ☐

10. $15 - 7 =$ ☐

11. $26 - 13 =$ ☐

12. $19 - 8 =$ ☐

13. $\begin{array}{r} 26 \\ -\ 7 \\ \hline \end{array}$	14. $\begin{array}{r} 32 \\ -14 \\ \hline \end{array}$	15. $\begin{array}{r} 38 \\ -19 \\ \hline \end{array}$	16. $\begin{array}{r} 64 \\ -21 \\ \hline \end{array}$	17. $\begin{array}{r} 73 \\ -25 \\ \hline \end{array}$
18. $\begin{array}{r} 97 \\ -46 \\ \hline \end{array}$	19. $\begin{array}{r} 87 \\ -49 \\ \hline \end{array}$	20. $\begin{array}{r} 132 \\ -\ 67 \\ \hline \end{array}$	21. $\begin{array}{r} 265 \\ -136 \\ \hline \end{array}$	22. $\begin{array}{r} 384 \\ -273 \\ \hline \end{array}$
23. $\begin{array}{r} 473 \\ -219 \\ \hline \end{array}$	24. $\begin{array}{r} 532 \\ -427 \\ \hline \end{array}$	25. $\begin{array}{r} 672 \\ -336 \\ \hline \end{array}$	26. $\begin{array}{r} 793 \\ -521 \\ \hline \end{array}$	27. $\begin{array}{r} 1894 \\ -\ 587 \\ \hline \end{array}$
28. $\begin{array}{r} 2759 \\ -\ 684 \\ \hline \end{array}$	29. $\begin{array}{r} 9483 \\ -3625 \\ \hline \end{array}$	30. $\begin{array}{r} 8642 \\ -3721 \\ \hline \end{array}$	31. $\begin{array}{r} 9876 \\ -7532 \\ \hline \end{array}$	32. $\begin{array}{r} 7058 \\ -4751 \\ \hline \end{array}$
33. $\begin{array}{r} 23821 \\ -15621 \\ \hline \end{array}$	34. $\begin{array}{r} 49373 \\ -27645 \\ \hline \end{array}$	35. $\begin{array}{r} 64537 \\ -32681 \\ \hline \end{array}$	36. $\begin{array}{r} 70156 \\ -34675 \\ \hline \end{array}$	37. $\begin{array}{r} 82163 \\ -64796 \\ \hline \end{array}$
38. $\begin{array}{r} 431528 \\ -308012 \\ \hline \end{array}$	39. $\begin{array}{r} 643081 \\ -521160 \\ \hline \end{array}$	40. $\begin{array}{r} 739414 \\ -638317 \\ \hline \end{array}$	41. $\begin{array}{r} 1804312 \\ -\ 262304 \\ \hline \end{array}$	42. $\begin{array}{r} 4340165 \\ -1275987 \\ \hline \end{array}$

Subtraction: Subtracting Across Zeros

Name _____

Subtract. Regroup as necessary.

1.
$$\begin{array}{r} 30 \\ -17 \\ \hline \end{array}$$

2.
$$\begin{array}{r} 60 \\ -32 \\ \hline \end{array}$$

3.
$$\begin{array}{r} 200 \\ -37 \\ \hline \end{array}$$

4.
$$\begin{array}{r} 100 \\ -68 \\ \hline \end{array}$$

5.
$$\begin{array}{r} 300 \\ -75 \\ \hline \end{array}$$

6.
$$\begin{array}{r} 5000 \\ -294 \\ \hline \end{array}$$

7.
$$\begin{array}{r} 600 \\ -436 \\ \hline \end{array}$$

8.
$$\begin{array}{r} 700 \\ -359 \\ \hline \end{array}$$

9.
$$\begin{array}{r} 9000 \\ -641 \\ \hline \end{array}$$

10.
$$\begin{array}{r} 2000 \\ -875 \\ \hline \end{array}$$

11.
$$\begin{array}{r} 4000 \\ -756 \\ \hline \end{array}$$

12.
$$\begin{array}{r} 3000 \\ -591 \\ \hline \end{array}$$

13.
$$\begin{array}{r} 10000 \\ -2586 \\ \hline \end{array}$$

14.
$$\begin{array}{r} 15000 \\ -9684 \\ \hline \end{array}$$

15.
$$\begin{array}{r} 20000 \\ -4969 \\ \hline \end{array}$$

16.
$$\begin{array}{r} 40000 \\ -28463 \\ \hline \end{array}$$

17.
$$\begin{array}{r} 60000 \\ -25695 \\ \hline \end{array}$$

18.
$$\begin{array}{r} 70000 \\ -28594 \\ \hline \end{array}$$

19.
$$\begin{array}{r} 100000 \\ -65263 \\ \hline \end{array}$$

20.
$$\begin{array}{r} 20000 \\ -3942 \\ \hline \end{array}$$

21.
$$\begin{array}{r} 80000 \\ -64328 \\ \hline \end{array}$$

22.
$$\begin{array}{r} 500000 \\ -385221 \\ \hline \end{array}$$

23.
$$\begin{array}{r} 200000 \\ -179496 \\ \hline \end{array}$$

24.
$$\begin{array}{r} 70000 \\ -39438 \\ \hline \end{array}$$

25.
$$\begin{array}{r} 70000 \\ -39999 \\ \hline \end{array}$$

26.
$$\begin{array}{r} 90000 \\ -48262 \\ \hline \end{array}$$

27.
$$\begin{array}{r} 1000000 \\ -875261 \\ \hline \end{array}$$

28.
$$\begin{array}{r} 5000000 \\ -3287324 \\ \hline \end{array}$$

Subtraction: Rounding & Estimating

Name _____

Part I: Round each number to the greatest place value position.

486 rounds to **500**   3,941 round to **4000**   7,364 rounds to **7000**

1. 128 _____

2. 674 _____

3. 389 _____

4. 443 _____

5. 369 _____

6. 987 _____

7. 2,612 _____

8. 6,543 _____

9. 7,107 _____

10. 8,972 _____

11. 7,432 _____

12. 8,460 _____

Part II: Round; then estimate the difference.

13. 247
   − 198

14. 234
   − 109

15. 630
   − 428

16. 421
   − 352

17. 632
   − 289

18. 732
   − 256

19. 810
   − 594

20. 949
   − 575

21. 8,425
   − 3,729

22. 7,258
   − 4,976

23. 5,460
   − 3,982

24. 12,984
   − 6,846

25. 32,788
   − 18,623

26. 18,752
   − 12,645

27. 90,800
   − 76,550

28. 88,718
   − 84,627

Subtraction: Problem Solving

Name _____

Solve each problem.

1. There are 87 students at Taylor's School who bring their lunches everyday. 65 of them always buy juice from the cafeteria. How many students do not buy juice?

2. Al played twenty-nine games of checkers on Friday and won twenty-six of them. On Saturday, he played thirty-two games. How many more games did he play on Saturday?

3. Kelly made 132 friendship bracelets on Friday. On Saturday, she made 88. How many more bracelets did she make on Friday?

4. Mark began reading a 598 page book on Monday. On Thursday, he was on page 213. How many pages does he have left?

5. Lee sold 485 roles of wrapping paper for the school fundraiser. Alice sold 326 rolls. How many more rolls of wrapping paper did Lee sell?

6. Mr. Moore drove his truck 4,878 miles for one week. The next week, he drove 2,572 miles. How many more miles did he drive in the first week?

7. Scott's dad is an airline pilot. He must reach 32,000 feet in the airplane before cruising. If he reaches 18,270 feet in the first twenty minutes after take-off, how many more feet must he climb?

1.

2.

3.

4.

5.

6.

7.

Multiplication: Basic Facts

Name _____

Part I: Find the product.

1. 6 × 8 = ☐   2. 11 × 6 = ☐   3. 9 × 8 = ☐   4. 10 × 12 = ☐

5. 9 × 5 = ☐   6. 2 × 12 = ☐   7. 12 × 6 = ☐   8. 11 × 11 = ☐

9. 11 × 7 = ☐   10. 9 × 11 = ☐   11. 11 × 10 = ☐   12. 12 × 7 = ☐

13. 5 × 10 = ☐   14. 8 × 12 = ☐   15. 6 × 7 = ☐   16. 8 × 10 = ☐

17. 9 × 9 = ☐   18. 12 × 9 = ☐   19. 11 × 8 = ☐   20. 5 × 4 = ☐

21. 7 × 5 = ☐   22. 12 × 12 = ☐   23. 10 × 10 = ☐   24. 11 × 12 = ☐

Part II: Find the missing factor.

25. 4 × ☐ = 32   26. 4 × ☐ = 48   27. ☐ × 6 = 60

28. 6 × ☐ = 54   29. ☐ × 11 = 55   30. 9 × ☐ = 90

31. 10 × ☐ = 70   32. ☐ × 8 = 56   33. 4 × ☐ = 28

34. ☐ × 5 = 40   35. 9 × ☐ = 36   36. 12 × ☐ = 36

37. 6 × ☐ = 36   38. ☐ × 8 = 24   39. ☐ × 9 = 27

40. 4 × ☐ = 40   41. ☐ × 6 = 42   42. ☐ × 7 = 63

43. ☐ × 11 = 44   44. 5 × ☐ = 30   45. 11 × ☐ = 44

Multiplication: Using Grouping Symbols   Name _____

Compute to find the final answer.

$(9 \times 4) \_ 2 = \boxed{}$

Think: $9 \times 4 = 36$ and $36 \times 2 = 72$; *therefore,* **72** *is the final product.*

$(7 \times 3) + 8 = \boxed{}$

Think: $7 \times 3 = 21$ and $21 + 8 = 29$; *therefore,* **29** *is the final solution.*

TIP: *Always work inside the parentheses first.*

---

1. $(9 \times 8) \times 3 = \boxed{}$

2. $(5 \_ 8) \_ 4 = \boxed{}$

3. $(5 \times 6) \times 8 = \boxed{}$

4. $7 \_ (6 \_ 8) = \boxed{}$

5. $7 \times (7 \times 6) = \boxed{}$

6. $9 \_ (5 \_ 5) = \boxed{}$

7. $(8 \times 4) \times (2 \times 8) = \boxed{}$

8. $(6 \_ 2) \_ (8 \_ 10) = \boxed{}$

9. $(3 \times 7) \times (9 \times 8) = \boxed{}$

10. $(7 \_ 3) \_ (8 \_ 2) = \boxed{}$

11. $(5 \times 10) + 10 = \boxed{}$

12. $(10 \_ 2) + (11 \_ 4) = \boxed{}$

13. $(4 \times 9) + 6 = \boxed{}$

14. $10 + (5 \_ 3) = \boxed{}$

15. $80 - (12 \times 5) = \boxed{}$

16. $(9 \_ 11) - \boxed{} =$

17. $(10 \times 11) \times 10 = \boxed{}$

18. $(12 \_ 4) + 18 = \boxed{}$

19. $(9 \times 9) - 1 = \boxed{}$

20. $(6 \_ 12) + (10 \_ 12) \boxed{}$

Multiplication: Multiplying Two-Digit and Three-Digit Numbers

Multiply.

Step 1:	Step 2:
3	3
Multiply ones, then regroup. 68	Multiply tens, then add extra tens. 68
× 4	× 4
2	272

1. 28
   × 4

2. 36
   × 5

3. 78
   × 6

4. 92
   × 7

5. 49
   × 9

6. 66
   × 8

7. 72
   × 5

8. 38
   × 4

9. 86
   × 7

10. 96
    × 5

11. 81
    × 8

12. 99
    × 9

13. 115
    × 7

14. 138
    × 5

15. 252
    × 3

16. 376
    × 7

17. 428
    × 4

18. 784
    × 8

19. 639
    × 7

20. 589
    × 2

21. 985
    × 4

22. 873
    × 2

23. 767
    × 6

24. 894
    × 5

25. 908
    × 7

26. 687
    × 9

27. 798
    × 8

28. 847
    × 6

Multiplication: Multiplying Three-Digit Numbers with Tens

Multiply.

> *First multiply ones by ones, tens, and hundreds.*
> *Next multiply tens by ones, tens and hundreds.*
> *Add the products to reach the final product.*
>
> | | | |
> |---|---|---|
> | 322 | 322 | 322 |
> | × 12 | × 12 | × 12 |
> | 644 | 644 | 644 |
> | | + 322 | + 322 |
> | | | 3,864 |

1. 213
    × 12

2. 326
    × 24

3. 252
    × 25

4. 267
    × 16

5. 389
    × 17

6. 427
    × 38

7. 455
    × 46

8. 538
    × 27

9. 625
    × 19

10. 781
    × 28

11. 847
    × 17

12. 778
    × 45

13. 465
    × 10

14. 632
    × 12

15. 741
    × 15

16. 896
    × 38

17. 527
    × 24

18. 837
    × 58

19. 964
    × 45

20. 971
    × 65

Multiplication: Multiplying Larger Numbers   Name _____

Multiply.

1. 4,328
    × 2

2. 6,493
    × 4

3. 7,231
    × 5

4. 4,784
    × 6

5. 5,624
    × 10

6. 4,819
    × 15

7. 5,672
    × 19

8. 7,468
    × 24

9. 14,684
    × 23

10. 23,413
     × 45

11. 42,387
     × 86

12. 64,309
     × 79

13. 15,343
     × 72

14. 16,748
     × 85

15. 29,064
     × 98

16. 38,424
     × 22

17. 65,207
     × 31

18. 72,256
     × 38

19. 85,212
     × 65

20. 94,368
     × 73

Multiplication: More Practice

Name _____

Multiply.

1. 46
    × 8

2. 75
    × 9

3. 87
    × 6

4. 95
    × 4

5. 103
    × 4

6. 127
    × 5

7. 159
    × 7

8. 186
    × 8

9. 94
    × 42

10. 86
    × 27

11. 45
    × 31

12. 88
    × 16

13. 278
    × 5

14. 326
    × 4

15. 418
    × 8

16. 532
    × 7

17. 685
    × 19

18. 741
    × 23

19. 846
    × 41

20. 976
    × 65

21. 1,372
    × 14

22. 2,426
    × 19

23. 3,874
    × 24

24. 5,646
    × 35

 THINK ABOUT IT!

25. Suzanne read 143 pages a week for 16 weeks. How many pages did she read?

MATH FACTS

Math is universal all over the earth because it is the basic science of nature. Human being did not create Math, we discovered Math through exploration, just like we discover new islands, animals and continents.

Multiplication: More Practice

Multiply.

1. 741
    × 55

2. 622
    × 80

3. 985
    × 96

4. 1,384
    × 25

5. 1,979
    × 31

6. 1,899
    × 41

7. 2,526
    × 38

8. 2,890
    × 52

9. 3,215
    × 62

10. 4,825
    × 72

11. 8,688
    × 35

12. 7,642
    × 79

13. 9,482
    × 58

14. 6,741
    × 46

15. 3,216
    × 28

16. 4,419
    × 33

17. 36,495
    × 68

18. 64,823
    × 46

19. 74,379
    × 82

20. 59,742
    × 70

21. 132,461
    × 33

22. 214,107
    × 42

23. 316,207
    × 52

24. 428,437
    × 63

Multiplication: Rounding to Estimate

Name _____

Round the top factor and leave the lower factor as is. Multiply to find the estimated product.

>
> $\begin{array}{r} 268 \\ \times\ \ 7 \end{array}$ rounds to **300.**   Therefore $300 \times 7 = 2100$.

1. $\begin{array}{r} 78 \\ \times\ 6 \end{array}$

2. $\begin{array}{r} 87 \\ \times\ 5 \end{array}$

3. $\begin{array}{r} 62 \\ \times\ 3 \end{array}$

4. $\begin{array}{r} 55 \\ \times\ 8 \end{array}$

5. $\begin{array}{r} 88 \\ \times\ 7 \end{array}$

6. $\begin{array}{r} 92 \\ \times\ 6 \end{array}$

7. $\begin{array}{r} 75 \\ \times\ 8 \end{array}$

8. $\begin{array}{r} 46 \\ \times\ 9 \end{array}$

9. $\begin{array}{r} 429 \\ \times\ \ 8 \end{array}$

10. $\begin{array}{r} 384 \\ \times\ \ 5 \end{array}$

11. $\begin{array}{r} 293 \\ \times\ \ 6 \end{array}$

12. $\begin{array}{r} 142 \\ \times\ \ 7 \end{array}$

13. $\begin{array}{r} 521 \\ \times\ \ 9 \end{array}$

14. $\begin{array}{r} 458 \\ \times\ \ 4 \end{array}$

15. $\begin{array}{r} 762 \\ \times\ \ 8 \end{array}$

16. $\begin{array}{r} 688 \\ \times\ \ 5 \end{array}$

17. $\begin{array}{r} 951 \\ \times\ \ 6 \end{array}$

18. $\begin{array}{r} 840 \\ \times\ \ 7 \end{array}$

19. $\begin{array}{r} 387 \\ \times\ \ 3 \end{array}$

20. $\begin{array}{r} 709 \\ \times\ \ 8 \end{array}$

THINK ABOUT IT!

21. If 138×5 is estimated, why is the estimated product lower than the exact product?

Multiplication: Estimation

Name _____

Round each factor to the greatest place value represented. Then, multiply to find the estimated product.

$$
\begin{array}{rcl}
325 & \longrightarrow & 300 \\
\times\,29 & \longrightarrow & \underline{30} \\
& & 9000
\end{array}
\qquad \text{and} \qquad
\begin{array}{rcl}
5{,}928 & \longrightarrow & 6{,}000 \\
\times\,120 & \longrightarrow & \times\,100 \\
& & 60{,}000
\end{array}
$$

1. 64
    × 21

2. 87
    × 33

3. 156
    × 46

4. 236
    × 55

5. 384
    × 25

6. 460
    × 31

7. 543
    × 68

8. 686
    × 75

9. 1,384
    × 35

10. 1,807
     × 41

11. 2,342
     × 63

12. 2,572
     × 48

13. 4,621
     × 39

14. 4,089
     × 56

15. 6,835
     × 43

16. 7,657
     × 66

17. 12,508
     × 89

18. 19,808
     × 94

19. 24,367
     × 77

20. 36,249
     × 96

Multiplication: Problem Solving

Name _____

Solve each problem.

1. Sonya made 7 pans of cupcakes for the school bake sale. Each pan held 12 cupcakes. How many cupcakes did Sonya make in all?

2. Wade ran 6 miles each day beginning on Monday, stopping on Friday. How many miles in all did he run those days?

3. Stephanie planted 12 rows of pansies. On each row she planted eight flowers. How many flowers did she plant?

4. Tom bought 7 boxes of adhesive labels. Each box contained 24 labels. How many labels did he have?

5. Dan's Donut Shop makes 35 donuts per minute. After six minutes, how many donuts have been made?

6. David can type 43 words per minute. How many words can he type in 11 minutes?

7. Caryn arranged 10 vases of flowers. In each vase she placed 12 roses. How many roses did she use in all?

8. Josh made 17 natural fruit drinks. He put 6 strawberries in each drink mixture. How many strawberries did he use to make all of the drinks?

9. Coco sold 36 rolls of wrapping paper each day for 15 days. She also sold 45 packages of bows for 13 days. **A.** How many rolls of wrapping paper did she sell? **B.** How many packages of bows did she sell?

1.

2.

3.

4.

5.

6.

7.

8.

9.

Multiplication: More Problem Solving

Name _____

Solve each problem.

1. Sandy sold 36 packages of candy for the school fundraiser. Each package contained 25 pieces of candy. How many pieces of candy did she sell?

2. Simon can make 45 origami cranes in an hour. He worked on a project making cranes for a week which totaled 16 hours. How many cranes did he make?

3. Donna decorated cookies with frosting and chocolate candy. Each cookie had six candies on top. If Donna made 146 cookies, how many chocolate candies did she use?

4. Roberd's Office Supply usually sells 98 packages of file folders per week. Each packagecontains 12 folders. How many folders do they sell each week?

5. Rachel labeled 64 test dishes in the science lab. She put 30 seeds in each dish to prepare for the experiment. How many seeds did she use?

6. Mr. Sims distributed 138 promotional packages for his company. Each package contained 48 pens, 62 calendars, and 40 note cards. How many calendars were distributed in the packages?

7. Melanie drove 218 miles each day of her trip for 13 days. At the end of her trip, how many miles had she driven?

8. Shelby bought 148 flats of spring plants. Each flat held 36 plants. How many plants did she buy?

1.

2.

3.

4.

5.

6.

7.

8.

Division: Basic Facts

Name _____

Part I: Find the quotient.

1. $99 \div 9 =$ ☐   2. $36 \div 3 =$ ☐   3. $120 \div 12 =$ ☐   4. $96 \div 8 =$ ☐

5. $28 \div 4 =$ ☐   6. $48 \div 8 =$ ☐   7. $24 \div 2 =$ ☐   8. $72 \div 6 =$ ☐

9. $72 \div 8 =$ ☐   10. $70 \div 10 =$ ☐   11. $12 \div 4 =$ ☐   12. $144 \div 12 =$ ☐

13. $60 \div 5 =$ ☐   14. $132 \div 12 =$ ☐   15. $49 \div 7 =$ ☐   16. $81 \div 9 =$ ☐

17. $36 \div 4 =$ ☐   18. $0 \div 12 =$ ☐   19. $80 \div 8 =$ ☐   20. $84 \div 7 =$ ☐

21. $20 \div 4 =$ ☐   22. $55 \div 11 =$ ☐   23. $45 \div 9 =$ ☐   24. $108 \div 9 =$ ☐

Part II: Find the missing number.

25. $63 \div$ ☐ $= 7$ 26. $35 \div$ ☐ $= 7$ 27. $64 \div 8 =$ ☐

28. $27 \div$ ☐ $= 9$ 29. $54 \div$ ☐ $= 9$ 30. $40 \div$ ☐ $= 8$

31. $50 \div$ ☐ $= 5$ 32. $24 \div 8 =$ ☐   33. $88 \div$ ☐ $= 11$

34. ☐ $\div 6 = 7$ 35. $60 \div$ ☐ $= 6$ 36. ☐ $\div 6 = 5$

37. $100 \div$ ☐ $= 10$ 38. ☐ $\div 7 = 7$ 39. $30 \div 3 =$ ☐

40. $56 \div$ ☐ $= 8$ 41. ☐ $\div 10 = 11$ 42. $48 \div$ ☐ $= 4$

43. $66 \div 11 =$ ☐   44. ☐ $\div 10 = 9$ 45. $121 \div 11 =$ ☐

Division: Using Grouping Symbols   Name _____

Divide to find the final solution.

$(42 \div 7) \div 3 = \boxed{}$

$(200 \div 50) + 12 = \boxed{}$

Think: $42 \div 7 = 6$ and $6 \div 3 = 2$; therefore, **2** is the final product.
Think: $200 \div 50 = 4$ and $4 + 12 = 16$; therefore, **16** is the final solution.

---

1. $(36 \div 2) \div 3 = \boxed{}$

2. $(72 \div 4) + 9 = \boxed{}$

3. $(98 \div 2) \div 7 = \boxed{}$

4. $3 \times (108 \div 9) = \boxed{}$

5. $(84 \div 4) \times 2 = \boxed{}$

6. $(70 \div 10) + (100 \div 25) = \boxed{}$

7. $(108 \div 9) + (36 \div 4) = \boxed{}$

8. $(75 \div 3) + (18 \div 6) = \boxed{}$

9. $(90 \div 3) + 6 = \boxed{}$

10. $(125 \div 25) + (70 \div 7) = \boxed{}$

11. $(81 \div 9) + (64 \div 8) = \boxed{}$

12. $(110 \div 10) + 57 = \boxed{}$

13. $(86 \div 2) - 20 = \boxed{}$

14. $(120 \div 12) \times (30 \div 5) = \boxed{}$

15. $(72 \div 6) \times (81 \div 9) = \boxed{}$

16. $(104 \div 2) + (90 \div 5) = \boxed{}$

17. $(132 \div 12) \times (108 \div 12) = \boxed{}$

18. $(60 \times 3) \div (36 \div 9) = \boxed{}$

19. $(99 \div 9) \times (45 \div 9) = \boxed{}$

20. $(120 \div 20) \times (120 \div 10) = \boxed{}$

Study how to divide 655 by 8.

Step 1:
$$\begin{array}{r} 8 \\ 8\overline{\smash{\big)}655} \\ -64 \\ \hline 1 \end{array}$$

Think: Divide the first 2 digits, **65 by 8.** The quotient is 8. Then, $8 \times 8 = 64$, and $65 - 64 = 1$.

Step 2:
$$\begin{array}{r} 81\ \mathbf{R7} \\ 8\overline{\smash{\big)}655} \\ -64 \\ \hline 15 \\ -8 \\ \hline \end{array}$$

Think: Bring the next number (5) down to the 1 ten which makes 15. Then divide 15 by 8. The quotient is 1, and $1 \times 8 = 8$. Finally, subtract 8 from 15 and the remainder is 7.

1. $5\overline{\smash{\big)}262}$ 2. $4\overline{\smash{\big)}389}$ 3. $6\overline{\smash{\big)}743}$ 4. $8\overline{\smash{\big)}598}$

5. $7\overline{\smash{\big)}964}$ 6. $5\overline{\smash{\big)}788}$ 7. $9\overline{\smash{\big)}894}$ 8. $7\overline{\smash{\big)}575}$

9. $8\overline{\smash{\big)}4{,}238}$ 10. $6\overline{\smash{\big)}3{,}895}$ 11. $5\overline{\smash{\big)}6{,}385}$ 12. $9\overline{\smash{\big)}8{,}642}$

13. $7\overline{\smash{\big)}5{,}784}$ 14. $8\overline{\smash{\big)}7{,}982}$ 15. $6\overline{\smash{\big)}8{,}650}$ 16. $10\overline{\smash{\big)}9{,}788}$

Division: Mixed Practice

Name _____

Divide.

1. $5\overline{)79}$ 2. $3\overline{)64}$ 3. $4\overline{)58}$ 4. $6\overline{)87}$

5. $4\overline{)132}$ 6. $6\overline{)155}$ 7. $7\overline{)208}$ 8. $3\overline{)256}$

9. $5\overline{)422}$ 10. $7\overline{)358}$ 11. $9\overline{)582}$ 12. $8\overline{)743}$

13. $6\overline{)2,382}$ 14. $3\overline{)4,017}$ 15. $4\overline{)3,286}$ 16. $6\overline{)5,664}$

17. $8\overline{)7,609}$ 18. $9\overline{)8,814}$ 19. $7\overline{)6,964}$ 20. $10\overline{)9,692}$

 THINK ABOUT IT!

21. Kim has 6,400 book club points saved up. For every 12 club points, she can order 1 free book. How many free books can she order with her points?

Division: Problem Solving

Solve each problem.

1. Mark had a board that was 72 feet long. If he cuts it every eight feet, how many boards will he have?

2. Sally had sixty-four eggs. She put them in sets of 4 for drying. How many sets did she have?

3. The school cafeteria has 152 chairs. Each table can accommodate 8 chairs. If all chairs are placed around tables, how many tables are needed?

4. Michele and Robin made 136 posters for the county fair. If they gave each business in town 4 posters, how many businesses were given posters?

5. Sam and John had collected 248 baseball cards. If they put them in groups of 8, how many groups will they have?

6. Mr. Blake ordered 400 new calculators for his store. The calculators are packed 16 per box. How many boxes were shipped?

7. Farmer Dole grew 1,080 stalks of corn. Each row had 54 stalks. How many rows did he plant?

8. Natalie collects glass beads. She keeps the beads in small containers that hold 14 beads each. If she has 392 beads, how many containers does she have?

9. Sonya has 496 cm of ribbon for her project. She needs to cut pieces that are 16 cm long. How many pieces will she have?

1.

2.

3.

4.

5.

6.

7.

8.

9.

Division: More Problem Solving

Name _____

Solve each problem.

1. Sue had 400 jelly beans. If she gives 10 to each of her friends at soccer practice, how many friends will receive jelly beans?

2. Monica printed 640 envelope labels. If each page had 33 labels, how many pages did she have?

3. Luke rode his bike 640 miles in the annual bike-a-thon. Each day he rode 32 miles. How many days did it take?

4. Carrie had a box of 636 pencils. If she puts them in groups of one dozen each, how many groups can she make?

5. Victor sold 744 drinks at the refreshment stand. If six drinks fit in one cup rack, how many racks did he use?

6. Mr. Keung had 1,875 corn plants to plant on his farm. If he plants 75 plants per row, how many rows will he have?

7. Paige addressed 1,350 invitations. If she completed them in only eighteen days, how many invitations did she address each day?

8. Leigh and Denise baked 1,750 brownies for their school's bake sale. They packed 20 in each box for the bake sale. How many packages did they make? How many brownies were left over?

9. Ray's Lighting Company packs 2,750 light bulbs into boxes. If each box can only hold 35 light bulbs, how many full boxes are packed?

1.	
2.	
3.	
4.	
5.	
6.	
7.	
8.	
9.	

Time: Finding Elapsed Time

Name _____

Directions: Find each time. All times for problems 1-6 are a.m.

1.

40 minutes after

_____

2.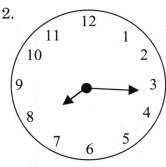

25 minutes before

_____

3.

35 minutes after

_____

4.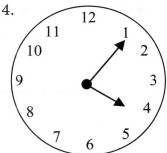

45 minutes after

_____

5.

35 minutes before

_____

6.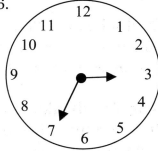

55 minutes before

_____

7. 35 minutes after 7:05 pm _____

8. 20 minutes after 8:10 a.m. _____

9. 1 hour and 35 minutes before 2:15 pm _____

10. 1 hour and 40 minutes after 8:15 a.m. _____

11. 25 minutes after 3:35 pm _____

12. 25 minutes before 5:45 am _____

13. 40 minutes after 3:50 pm _____

14. 10 minutes after 11:50 am _____

 THINK ABOUT IT!

15. If John walks to work at 8:15 am, and it takes him 25 minutes, what time will he arrive at work?

Time: Estimating Time

Name _____

Directions: Estimate each time. All of the times shown are morning times (a.m.).

1 hour earlier _____

Think: 8:45 a.m. is closer to 9:00 a.m. So, one hour earlier is about 8:00 a.m.

1.

4 hours later

_____

2.

3 hours later

_____

3.

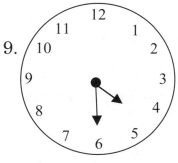

1 hour before

_____

4.

5 hours after

_____

5.

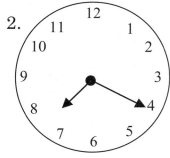

4 hours later

_____

6.

2 hours, 15 minutes later _____

7.

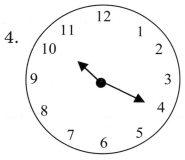

$3\frac{1}{2}$ hours after

8.

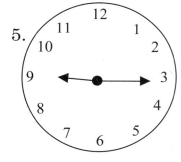

4 hours later

_____

9.

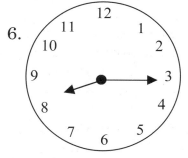

3 hours, 30 minutes later _____

Time: Problem Solving

Name _____

Solve each problem.

1. Lynn takes piano lessons at 2:00 p.m.. If she has 1 lesson for an hour and her trip takes her 30 minutes one way, how long is she gone?

2. Meg can get to work in 45 minutes. If her returntrip takes 1 hour and fifteen minutes, how long does her travel take?

3. Zachary wakes up at 6:45 a.m. He eats breakfast at 7:00. He brushes his teeth at 7:20 and is on the bus by 7:35. How long does this routine take?

4. Juan goes to the park at 2:15 p.m.. If he returns 3 hours later, what time does he return?

5. Tracy rides her bike each day for 1 ½ hours. If she starts at 3:30 p.m., when will she finish?

6. Darriel leaves his house at 1:30 p.m. He arrives at the airport at 2:00 p.m. His flight departs at 2:45 p.m. The plane lands at 4:15 p.m. How long was his flight?

7. Sandy left her grandparents house at 4:30 p.m. The trip back home takes 2 hours and 40 minutes. What time will Sandy arrive home?

8. Mr. Sellers leaves his office at 9:00 a.m. for a two-hour meeting. His meeting is 45 minutes away. What time will he return to his office?

9. Rachel's first period class starts at 7:30 a.m. It is 55 minutes long. If her second and third period classes are 55 minutes long, what time will it be at the end of her third period class?

1.

2.

3.

4.

5.

6.

7.

8.

9.

Money: Multiplying Money

Name _____

Solve each problem.

1. $4.95
   ×   7

2. $6.35
   ×   6

3. $7.42
   ×   9

4. $9.92
   ×   8

5. $15.48
   ×   8

6. $25.72
   ×   9

7. $39.74
   ×   7

8. $45.64
   ×   6

9. $75.36
   ×   7

10. $86.13
    ×   6

11. $98.55
    ×   4

12. $136.09
    ×   5

13. $182.36
    ×   6

14. $218.94
    ×   9

15. $254.98
    ×   6

16. $365.24
    ×   8

17. $432.46
    ×   7

18. $564.30
    ×   5

19. $674.86
    ×   9

20. $2,426.08
    ×   4

21. $1,228.08
    ×   4

22. $3,123.45
    ×   5

23. $1,386.29
    ×   7

24. $3,498.58
    ×   8

 ## THINK ABOUT IT!

25. Barry buys 3 collector pens for $21.95 each.
    How much money does he spend on the pens?

Money: Dividing Money

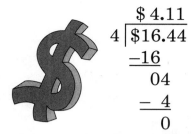

$$\begin{array}{r} \$4.11 \\ 4\overline{)\$16.44} \\ -16 \\ \hline 04 \\ -4 \\ \hline 0 \end{array}$$

Think: Divide $16.44 by 4 as you would whole numbers. Place the decimal in the quotient directly above its place in the dividend. Place the $ sign to *left* of the dollar amount.

1. $7\overline{)\$14.21}$ 2. $6\overline{)\$15.12}$ 3. $5\overline{)\$19.05}$ 4. $9\overline{)\$29.34}$

5. $6\overline{)\$31.68}$ 6. $8\overline{)\$39.60}$ 7. $9\overline{)\$47.52}$ 8. $7\overline{)\$56.77}$

9. $8\overline{)\$44.48}$ 10. $7\overline{)\$70.56}$ 11. $6\overline{)\$49.38}$ 12. $5\overline{)\$43.25}$

13. $4\overline{)\$98.20}$ 14. $5\overline{)\$85.05}$ 15. $8\overline{)\$99.28}$ 16. $7\overline{)\$123.52}$

17. $8\overline{)\$258.96}$ 18. $9\overline{)\$538.92}$ 19. $7\overline{)\$652.61}$ 20. $5\overline{)\$828.95}$

Money: Problem Solving

Name _____

Solve each problem.

1. Sammy bought a football for $26.95, a stopwatch for $18.95 and a watchband for $7.59. How much did he spend?

2. Mrs. Cook bought 15 plants for her yard. She paid $14.95 per plant. How much did she spend?

3. Taylor made 36 bracelets. She sold them for $18.95 each. How much did she make from the sale of the bracelets?

4. Hong purchased 45 fortune cookie packages for his family's restaurant. He paid $12.85 per package. How much did Hong spend?

5. Maryann sold 64 Valentine gifts at her gift shop. The gifts were specially priced at $17.95. How much did she receive from the sale of the gifts?

6. Mario bought 3 vacation souvenirs at $25.35 each, 2 at $14.95 and one at $8.50. How much did he spend in all?

7. Valerie's grandmother bought 22 antique silver pieces at the auction. Each item was $125.00. How much did she spend?

8. Mrs. Walker was purchasing party favors for her daughter's birthday party. The party favors totaled $2.87 per person. Her daughter invited 18 friends to her party. How much did Mrs. Walker spend on party favors for 18 friends?

9. Tawana made $55.75 from her babysitting jobs. She spent $44.95 on a pair of shoes. How much did she have left over?

1.

2.

3.

4.

5.

6.

7.

8.

9.

Geometry: Basic Figures

Name _____

Part I: Name each figure.

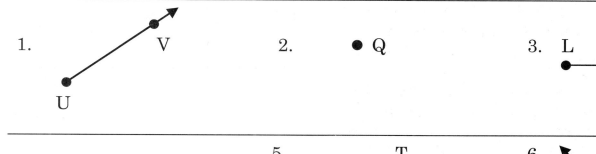

Write as	Point A	$\overline{CD}$ or $\overline{DC}$	$\overleftrightarrow{EF}$ or $\overleftrightarrow{FE}$	$\overrightarrow{GH}$
Read as	Point A	Segment CD or DC	Line EF or FE	Ray GH

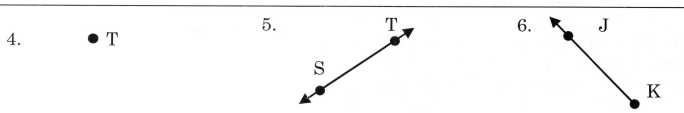

1.

 V

 U

2. • Q

3. L ————— M

4. • T

5. S —— T

6. J —— K

Part II: Draw and label an example for each of the following.

7. line BA

8. ray AB

9. point E

10. line segment XY

11. line NO

12. ray RS

 THINK ABOUT IT!

13. How many end points do each of the following have?
   a. a line segment   b. a ray   c. a line

Geometry: Polygons

Tell whether each figure is a polygon. If yes, write its name.

A **polygon** is a closed plane figure with 3 or more sides.

This is a quadrilateral.

1.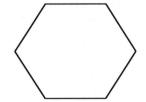

2.

3.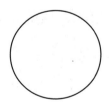

4.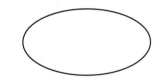

5.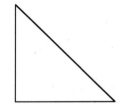

6.

7.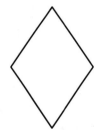

8.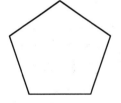

9.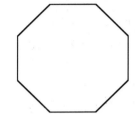

 THINK ABOUT IT!

10. What polygons would you have if you traced the faces of each polyhedron?

    a.   b.

Geometry: Angles

Classify each angle as acute, right, or obtuse.

Acute Angle
less than 90°

Right Angle
equals 90°

Obtuse Angle
more than 90°
but less than 180°

1.

2.

3.

4.

5.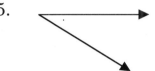

6.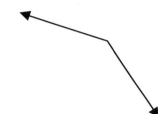

7.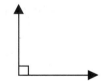

8.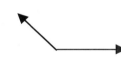

9.

10.

11.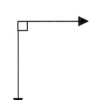

12.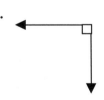

 THINK ABOUT IT!

13. In an acute angle, what is the greatest possible whole number of degrees? What about in an obtuse angle?

MATH FACTS

Scientists who make maps of mountains or the oceans use mathematics to create their images. This makes exploration such as finding ships on the ocean floor or mining the sea for minerals easier.

Geometry: Triangles

Name _____

List all the names for each triangle.

Classified
by sides:

<u>Equilateral</u>

3 equal sides

<u>Isosceles</u>

2 equal sides

<u>Scalene</u>

no equal sides

Classified
by angles:

<u>Acute</u>

3 acute angles

<u>Obtuse</u>

1 obtuse angle

<u>Right</u>

1 right angle

1.

2.

3.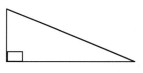

4.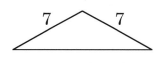

5.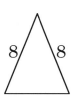

6.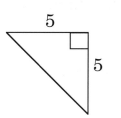

 THINK ABOUT IT!

7. For each statement, write *always*, *sometimes*, or *never*.

_____ a. A right triangle is an equilateral triangle.

_____ b. An equilateral triangle is an acute triangle.

_____ c. An obtuse triangle is a scalene triangle.

Geometry: Circles

Name _____

Study these terms below to answer the questions.

center:	point used to name the circle; center of the circle.
radius:	a segment from the center of the circle to any point on the circle.
diameter:	a segment passing through the center with both endpoints on the circle.
chord:	a segment with both end points on the circle that does not pass through the center.
central angle:	an angle whose vertex is the center of the circle.

Use the figure at the right to answer questions 1-7.

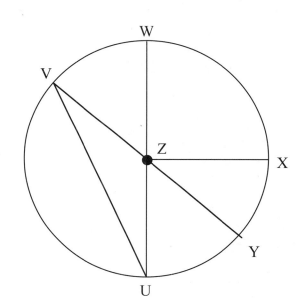

1. Name the center.

2. Name each radius.

3. Name each diameter.

4. Name each chord.

5. Name each central angle.

6. Name an angle that is not a central angle.

7. How does the length of a radius compare to the length of a diameter?

 THINK ABOUT IT!

8. Is it possible for a circle to have more than one
   a. center   b. radius   c. diameter   d. chord

Geometry: Perimeter

Name _____

Find the perimeter of each figure.

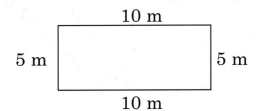

Perimeter: *distance around each figure*

To find the **perimeter**, add the lengths of the sides: $10 + 5 + 10 + 5 = 30$ m

---

1.
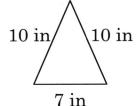

2.
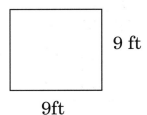

3.
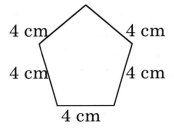

4.
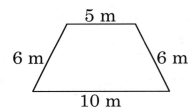

5.
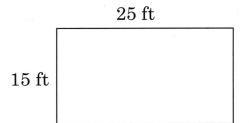

6.
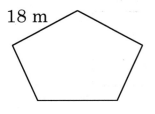

All sides are equal.

 THINK ABOUT IT!

7. One room is 17 feet long by 16 feet wide. Another room is 12 feet long by 20 feet wide. Which room has the greater perimeter?

Geometry: Area
Find the area of each figure.

Name _____

Area: *number of square units inside a figure*

15 in

5 in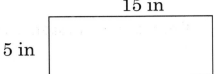

To find the area of rectangles and squares, multiply the length times the width.

$5 \times 15 = 75$ in^2

1.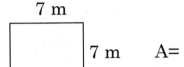
7 m

7 m   A=

2.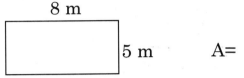
8 m

5 m   A=

3.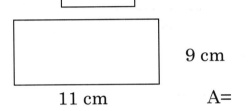
9 cm

11 cm   A=

4.
9 cm

9 cm   A=

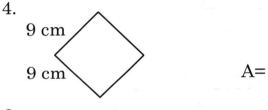

5.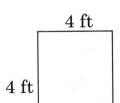
7 m

6 m   A=

6.
10 yd   A=

3 yd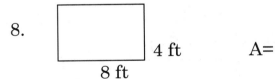

7.
4 ft

4 ft   A=

8.
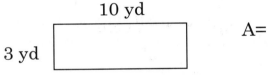
4 ft   A=

8 ft

💡 **THINK ABOUT IT!**

9. If the length and width of the rectangle below was doubled, do you think its area would double? Explain.

2 m

4 m

Geometry: Problem Solving

Name _____

Solve each problem.

1. What type of angle is formed on a clock when it is 10 o'clock?

2. What could be the least number of degrees in an obtuse angle? The greatest?

3. In the diagram below, if one side of the square is 10 ft long, what is the length of the radius of the circle?

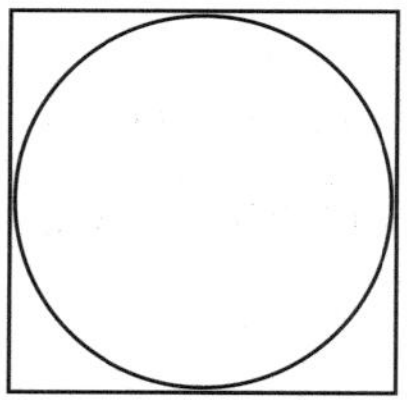

4. Is it possible for an isosceles triangle to also be an equilateral triangle? Explain.

5. Are there any acute angles in an obtuse triangle? Are there any obtuse angles in an acute triangle?

6. Find the perimeter of a six-sided figure if all sides equal 4 ft 5 in.

7. Casey is putting chicken wire around her garden. If the garden is 5 ft long by 4 ft wide, how much chicken wire will she need to purchase?

8. The area of a rectangle is 16 cm^2. If one side equals 8 cm, what is the perimeter of the rectangle?

1.

2.

3.

4.

5.

6.

7.

8.

Decimals: Tenths, Hundredths

Part I: For each problem, write a decimal.

five hundredths = 0.05   **two and four thousandths = 2.004**

1. two tenths

2. nine tenths

3. seven hundredths

4. twelve hundredths

5. ten and two tenths

6. nine thousandths

7. twenty-five hundredths

8. five and forty-one thousandths

9. five and four hundredths

10. three and three thousandths

11. thirty-one and one tenth

12. four hundred and five thousandths

Part II: Write each decimal in words.

1.72 = one and seventy-two hundredths   0.056 = fifty-six thousandths

13. 0.08

14. 0.008

15. 2.052

16. 10.11

17. 0.325

18. 3.052

19. 0.25

20. 0.015

21. 4.197

22. 6.053

23. 5.53

24. 16.037

25. 0.902

26. 21.143

27. 53.281

Decimals: Comparing and Ordering

Name _____

Write >, <, or = for each ◯.

8.47 ◯ 8.46

↓

8.47
8.46

     7 > 6   so   8.47 > 8.46

To compare 2 or more decimals:
1. Line up the decimal point.
2. Compare digits from *left to right* in their corresponding place value.

---

1.   0.7 ◯ 0.4

2.   2.04 ◯ 2.4

3.   0.62 ◯ 0.26

4.   0.2 ◯ 0.22

5.   0.9 ◯ 0.90

6.   1.06 ◯ 1.60

7.   4.03 ◯ 4.003

8.   0.0005 ◯ 0.005

Order from least to greatest.

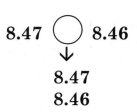

9.   0.3, 0.5, 0.1

10.   3.7, 3.5, 3.8

11.   4.5, 4.52, 4.052

12.   0.6, 0.06, 0.006

13.   2.05, 2.5, 0.5, 0.05

14.   0.62, 0.621, 0.625, 0.612

 THINK ABOUT IT!

15. Write a decimal between:
    a. 0.4 and 0.25   b. 15.5 and 15.4   c. 0.06 and 0.07

Decimals: Rounding & Estimating   **Name** _____

Part I: Round each decimal to the underlined place value. Study the examples.

1_3_.6 ⟶ **14** ◄   Look to the right of the **3**. If that number is
                          5 or greater, ***round up***. If not, keep the
6._3_5 ⟶ **6.4** ◄   number the same.

---

1. _3_.9   2. 8._5_4   3. _6_.1
    _____   _____   _____

4. 0._6_3   5. 10._0_5   6. _3_.82
    _____   _____   _____

7. 4.3_7_1   8. 9.9_5_3   9. 6.5_3_2
    _____   _____   _____

10. _8_.08   11. 8.8_1_7   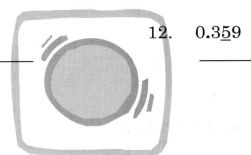   12. 0.3_5_9
    _____   _____   _____

Part II: Estimate each answer.

11.98 ⟶ 12   1. Round each number to the nearest whole number.
−5.13   −5   2. Add or subtract.
Estimate   **7**

---

13. 5.4   14. 19.1   15. 2.2   16. 27.6
    +4.8   − 8.9   + 6.9   − 6.2

17. 16.74   18. 19.38   19. 16.50   20. 12.5
    −12.87   + 15.77   − 13.90   + 16.8

Decimals: Adding

Add.

15.6 + 27.63

$$15.60$$
$$+\ 27.63$$
$$43.23$$

1. Line up the decimal points
2. Add zeros if necessary.
3. Add as with whole numbers
4. Carry if necessary.

TIP: *Remember to bring your decimal point down into your answer.*

---

1. 0.6
    + 0.4

2. 3.65
    + 2.43

3. 4.37
    + 1.44

4. 3.01
    + 8.72

5. 13.42
    + 24.79

6. 21.3
    + 17.5

7. 6.09
    + 2.51

8. 3.89
    + 9.59

9. 0.74
    + 0.48

10. 33.34
     + 17.26

11. 0.36
     + 0.19

12. 5.725
     + 3.169

13. 11.8 + 12 =

14. 7.91 + 11.4 =

15. 0.5 + 5.95 =

16. 13.9 + 326.7 =

17. 65.70 + 15.33 =

18. 16.84 + 17.91 =

19. 3.528 + 4.56 =

20. 14.2 + 8.62 =

21. 60.5 + 9.176 =

 THINK ABOUT IT!

22. Rachel went shopping for a new outfit. She found a sweater for $25.95 and a pair of pants for $19.95. How much money did she spend?

Decimals: Subtracting

Subtract.

13.6 − 11.92

$$
\begin{array}{r}
13.60 \\
-\,11.92 \\
\hline
1.68
\end{array}
$$

1. Line up the decimal points.
2. Add zeros if necessary.
3. Subtract as with whole numbers.
4. Trade if necessary.

TIP: *Remember to bring your decimal point down into your answer.*

1. $\begin{array}{r} 0.8 \\ -\,0.5 \\ \hline \end{array}$

2. $\begin{array}{r} 8.75 \\ -\,2.43 \\ \hline \end{array}$

3. $\begin{array}{r} 6.47 \\ -\,1.44 \\ \hline \end{array}$

4. $\begin{array}{r} 7.01 \\ -\,5.72 \\ \hline \end{array}$

5. $\begin{array}{r} 15.52 \\ -\,14.79 \\ \hline \end{array}$

6. $\begin{array}{r} 31.3 \\ -\,17.65 \\ \hline \end{array}$

7. $\begin{array}{r} 8.08 \\ -\,2.51 \\ \hline \end{array}$

8. $\begin{array}{r} 5.89 \\ -\,3.59 \\ \hline \end{array}$

9. $\begin{array}{r} 0.92 \\ -\,0.87 \\ \hline \end{array}$

10. $\begin{array}{r} 43.34 \\ -\,18.26 \\ \hline \end{array}$

11. $\begin{array}{r} 0.46 \\ -\,0.29 \\ \hline \end{array}$

12. $\begin{array}{r} 8.725 \\ -\,4.367 \\ \hline \end{array}$

13. 12.8 − 10 =

14. 8.91 − 7.65 =

15. 0.89 − 0.6 =

16. 23.9 − 16.7 =

17. 75.7 − 14.33 =

18. 19.84 − 16.91 =

19. 7.528 − 4.569 =

20. 17.2 − 8.72 =

21. 70.5 − 12.176 =

 THINK ABOUT IT!

22. Stacey needs $49 for a new pair of sneakers. She has saved $8.75, $12.50, and $10.50 from babysitting. How much more money does she need?

Decimals: Multiplying

Find each product.

Factor	.4	1 dec. place
Factor	× .6	1 dec. place
Product	.24	2 dec. places

1. Multiply as you would whole numbers.

2. The number of decimal places in the product is the sum of the decimal places in the factors.

TIP: *When the problem is presented horizontally (see the one below), make sure to line up the numbers on the right. Do not line up the decimal points.*

$$.58 \times 0.7$$

Correct

$$\begin{array}{r} .58 \\ \times\ 0.7 \\ \hline \end{array}$$

Incorrect

$$\begin{array}{r} .58 \\ \times 0.7\ \underline{\quad} \\ \end{array}$$

---

1. $$\begin{array}{r} .8 \\ \times 4 \\ \hline \end{array}$$

2. $$\begin{array}{r} .5 \\ \times .7 \\ \hline \end{array}$$

3. $$\begin{array}{r} 3.9 \\ \times\ 0.7 \\ \hline \end{array}$$

4. $$\begin{array}{r} 3.17 \\ \times\ 0.9 \\ \hline \end{array}$$

5. $$\begin{array}{r} 2.54 \\ \times\ \ \ 7 \\ \hline \end{array}$$

6. $$\begin{array}{r} .04 \\ \times .96 \\ \hline \end{array}$$

7. $$\begin{array}{r} 9.1 \\ \times .22 \\ \hline \end{array}$$

8. $$\begin{array}{r} 2.9 \\ \times 6.4 \\ \hline \end{array}$$

9. $$\begin{array}{r} 6.39 \\ \times .65 \\ \hline \end{array}$$

10. $$\begin{array}{r} 45.1 \\ \times .002 \\ \hline \end{array}$$

11. $$\begin{array}{r} 8.23 \\ \times .004 \\ \hline \end{array}$$

12. $$\begin{array}{r} 35.2 \\ \times 4.95 \\ \hline \end{array}$$

13. $43 \times 3.7 =$

14. $4.3 \times 3.7 =$

15. $0.43 \times 3.7 =$

16. $0.43 \times 0.37 =$

17. $0.04 \times 0.03 =$

18. $0.051 \times 6 =$

19. $0.15 \times 0.05 =$

20. $42 \times 0.006 =$

Decimals: Dividing

Name _____

Find each quotient.

$$34.5 \div 5$$

$$5\overline{)34.5}^{\,\bullet} \quad \longleftarrow$$ 1. Bring the decimal point up into the quotient.

$$\begin{array}{r} 6.9 \\ 5\overline{)34.5} \\ \underline{30} \\ 45 \\ \underline{45} \\ 0 \end{array} \quad \longleftarrow$$ 2. Divide as you would with whole numbers.

---

1. $2\overline{)8.4}$

2. $3\overline{)33.69}$

3. $4\overline{)24.92}$

4. $6\overline{)5.166}$

5. $5\overline{)20.95}$

6. $7\overline{)32.34}$

7. $8\overline{)40.8}$

8. $6\overline{)14.4}$

9. $8\overline{)27.2}$

10. $2\overline{)274.72}$

11. $7\overline{)125.72}$

12. $5\overline{)338.85}$

13. $9\overline{)310.5}$

14. $9\overline{)0.756}$

15. $4\overline{)3262.4}$

16. $8\overline{)6.304}$

Decimals: Problem Solving

Name _____

Solve each problem.

1. As time on a digital stopwatch goes from 1.25to 1.76 seconds, how many times has the hundredths digit changed? the tenths digit?

2. A decimal is between 5.61 and 5.71. When rounded to the nearest tenth, the answer is 5.6. What could the decimal be?

3. At the grocery store, Susie's mom buys milk for $1.89, eggs for $0.99, and a loaf of bread for $1.29. About how money has she spent?

4. At the Lunch-n-Dine, hamburgers cost $1.79 each. A grilled chicken sandwich cost $2.09. If Stacy and her friend each order a chicken sandwich, what is the total cost of both sandwiches?

5. A CD cost $13.95. If Sharon gave the cashier $15.00, what will her change be?

6. Eric has saved $22.75 toward a new pair of sneakers. If the sneakers cost $49.99, how much money does Eric still need?

7. On Saturday, Nancy Ann worked from 8:30 – 5:30 at her part time job. She was not paid for the one hour lunch break. If she earns $6.25 an hour, how much money did she earn?

8. If you were to divide $28.50 among four people, how many dollar bills would each person receive?

1.

2.

3.

4.

5.

6.

7.

8.

Fractions: Simplifying Fractions

Name _____

Reduce to lowest terms.

$\dfrac{6}{12}$

To reduce a fraction to lowest terms, divide its numerator and denominator by their GCF.

$\dfrac{6}{12}\big]\dfrac{6}{6} = \dfrac{1}{2}$

TIP: *You know a fraction is in lowest terms when the GCF of its numerator and Denominator is 1.*

---

1. $\dfrac{7}{21}$

2. $\dfrac{3}{6}$

3. $\dfrac{9}{12}$

4. $\dfrac{5}{25}$

5. $\dfrac{6}{9}$

6. $\dfrac{16}{20}$

7. $\dfrac{4}{10}$

8. $\dfrac{9}{14}$

9. $\dfrac{12}{21}$

10. $\dfrac{9}{24}$

11. $\dfrac{8}{15}$

12. $\dfrac{18}{27}$

13. $\dfrac{5}{10}$

14. $\dfrac{16}{24}$

15. $\dfrac{3}{10}$

16. $\dfrac{21}{42}$

17. $\dfrac{30}{36}$

18. $\dfrac{16}{28}$

19. $\dfrac{60}{100}$

20. $\dfrac{12}{25}$

21. $\dfrac{15}{40}$

22. $\dfrac{62}{75}$

23. $\dfrac{75}{100}$

24. $\dfrac{30}{80}$

 THINK ABOUT IT!

25. If both the numerator and denominator of a fraction are even, can the fraction be in lowest terms? Explain.

MATH FACTS

A newer branch of mathematics discovered by Benoit Mandelbrot, is called "Fractal Theory." This area studies the repeating patterns found in nature such as the spots on a cow or the puffiness of clouds. Weather forecasting and medicine may benefit from this.

Fractions: Fractions and Decimals

Name _____

$\dfrac{2}{5}$

$2 \div 5 = .1$

To change a fraction to a decimal, divide the numerator by the denominator.

---

1. $\dfrac{1}{2}$

2. $\dfrac{3}{20}$

3. $\dfrac{4}{10}$

4. $\dfrac{3}{5}$

5. $\dfrac{1}{4}$

6. $\dfrac{7}{10}$

7. $\dfrac{60}{100}$

8. $\dfrac{4}{50}$

9. $\dfrac{2}{10}$

10. $\dfrac{4}{5}$

11. $\dfrac{6}{20}$

12. $\dfrac{5}{25}$

13. $\dfrac{18}{50}$

14. $\dfrac{9}{10}$

15. $\dfrac{17}{100}$

16. $\dfrac{3}{4}$

Part II: Write each decimal as a fraction or mixed number in simplest form.

$$0.5 = \text{five tenths} = \dfrac{5}{10} \qquad\qquad 2.7 = 2\dfrac{7}{10}$$

---

17. 0.3

18. 0.9

19. 0.7

20. 0.1

21. 0.44

22. 0.56

23. 1.32

24. 2.53

25. 12.6

26. 4.15

27. 7.05

28. 20.07

Name _____

Fractions: Improper Fractions & Mixed Numbers

Part I: Write each improper fraction as a mixed number or a whole number.

$$\frac{27}{6}$$

1. Divide the numerator by the denominator.

$$6\overline{)27} \quad \begin{array}{c} 4 \\ \end{array}$$
$$\underline{24}$$

2. If there is a remainder, put it in fraction form over the *divisor*.

3. ***Reduce fraction to lowest terms.***

$$3 = 4\frac{3}{6} = 4\frac{1}{2}$$

1. $\frac{24}{10}$ 2. $\frac{16}{5}$ 3. $\frac{17}{2}$ 4. $\frac{30}{7}$ 5. $\frac{48}{9}$

6. $\frac{65}{20}$ 7. $\frac{60}{3}$ 8. $\frac{58}{8}$ 9. $\frac{25}{6}$ 10. $\frac{360}{36}$

11. $\frac{60}{24}$ 12. $\frac{147}{12}$ 13. $\frac{19}{3}$ 14. $\frac{40}{12}$ 15. $\frac{80}{20}$

Part II: Write each mixed number as an improper fraction.

$$5\frac{1}{3}$$

1. Multiply the whole number by the denominator.

$$5 \times 3 + 1 = \frac{16}{3}$$

2. Add the numerator.

3. Place that number over the denominator.

16. $2\frac{3}{4}$ 17. $4\frac{2}{3}$ 18. $3\frac{2}{5}$ 19. $1\frac{7}{8}$ 20. $2\frac{3}{8}$

21. $4\frac{5}{6}$ 22. $7\frac{2}{5}$ 23. $1\frac{3}{4}$ 24. $8\frac{2}{4}$ 25. $6\frac{4}{7}$

26. $5\frac{1}{5}$ 27. $6\frac{7}{9}$ 28. $4\frac{1}{2}$ 29. $5\frac{2}{7}$ 30. $7\frac{3}{4}$

Fractions: Lowest Common Denominator   Name _____

Rewrite each pair of fractions using the least common denominator.

$\dfrac{2}{3}$, $\dfrac{1}{4}$ 1. Find the lowest common multiple (LCM) of the denominator.

LCM = 12   2. Rewrite the fractions using the LCM.

$\dfrac{2 \times 4}{3 \times 4} = \dfrac{8}{12}$

$\dfrac{1 \times 3}{4 \times 3} = \dfrac{3}{12}$ $\dfrac{8}{12}$, $\dfrac{3}{12}$

TIP: *Remember to multiply both the numerator and denominator by the LCM.*

1. $\dfrac{2}{5}$, $\dfrac{1}{3}$ 2. $\dfrac{3}{4}$, $\dfrac{3}{8}$ 3. $\dfrac{1}{2}$, $\dfrac{1}{6}$

4. $\dfrac{1}{4}$, $\dfrac{7}{10}$ 5. $\dfrac{5}{6}$, $\dfrac{2}{3}$ 6. $\dfrac{3}{4}$, $\dfrac{1}{2}$

7. $\dfrac{3}{4}$, $\dfrac{2}{5}$ 8. $\dfrac{2}{9}$, $\dfrac{1}{6}$ 9. $\dfrac{1}{3}$, $\dfrac{3}{4}$

10. $\dfrac{3}{5}$, $\dfrac{3}{7}$ 11. $\dfrac{4}{9}$, $\dfrac{11}{12}$ 12. $\dfrac{7}{8}$, $\dfrac{11}{12}$

13. $\dfrac{3}{4}$, $\dfrac{9}{16}$ 14. $\dfrac{4}{5}$, $\dfrac{11}{12}$ 15. $\dfrac{7}{15}$, $\dfrac{3}{5}$

16. $\dfrac{1}{2}$, $\dfrac{5}{6}$, $\dfrac{3}{4}$ 17. $\dfrac{2}{3}$, $\dfrac{3}{8}$, $\dfrac{1}{4}$ 18. $\dfrac{3}{10}$, $\dfrac{7}{12}$, $\dfrac{11}{15}$

 THINK ABOUT IT!

19. When rewriting two fractions with common denominators, why is it an advantage to use the least common denominator?

Name _____

Fractions: Adding and Subtracting with Like Denominators

Find each sum or difference. Write all answers in lowest terms.

$3\frac{1}{8}$
$+ 1\frac{3}{8}$
_____

$4\frac{4}{8} = 4\frac{1}{2}$

1. Add or subtract the whole numbers if there are any.

2. Add or subtract the numerators of the fractions. Place over their common denominators.

3. Reduce if necessary.

---

1. $\frac{3}{7}$
$+ \frac{2}{7}$
_____

2. $\frac{1}{5}$
$+ \frac{2}{5}$
_____

3. $\frac{7}{8}$
$- \frac{3}{8}$
_____

4. $\frac{1}{6}$
$+ \frac{2}{6}$
_____

5. $\frac{3}{4}$
$- \frac{1}{4}$
_____

6. $\frac{9}{12}$
$- \frac{5}{12}$
_____

7. $\frac{7}{8}$
$+ \frac{1}{8}$
_____

8. $\frac{3}{6}$
$- \frac{1}{6}$
_____

9. $\frac{17}{20}$
$- \frac{13}{20}$
_____

10. $\frac{14}{24}$
$+ \frac{10}{24}$
_____

11. $\frac{1}{8}$
$+ \frac{4}{8}$
_____

12. $\frac{5}{6}$
$- \frac{3}{6}$
_____

13. $4\frac{1}{6}$
$+ 5\frac{3}{6}$
_____

14. $20\frac{7}{8}$
$- 15\frac{7}{8}$
_____

15. $6\frac{1}{4}$
$+ 16\frac{2}{4}$
_____

16. $9\frac{7}{10}$
$- 8\frac{5}{10}$
_____

Fractions: Adding and Subtracting

Find each sum or difference. Write all answers in lowest terms.

$$\frac{2}{3} \times \frac{4}{4} = \frac{8}{12}$$
$$+ \frac{1}{4} \times \frac{3}{3} = \frac{3}{12}$$
$$\frac{11}{12}$$

1. Find the lowest common denominator, also known as the LCD, of both denominators.
2. Write equivalent fractions using the LCD.
3. Add or subtract the fractions, and reduce if necessary.

1. $\frac{7}{12}$
  $- \frac{1}{4}$

2. $\frac{1}{8}$
  $+ \frac{5}{6}$

3. $\frac{2}{5}$
  $- \frac{2}{7}$

4. $\frac{7}{8}$
  $+ \frac{3}{4}$

5. $\frac{2}{3}$
  $- \frac{1}{10}$

6. $\frac{2}{5}$
  $+ \frac{2}{3}$

7. $\frac{4}{9}$
  $- \frac{1}{4}$

8. $\frac{3}{4}$
  $+ \frac{1}{3}$

9. $\frac{5}{8}$
  $+ \frac{3}{4}$

10. $\frac{5}{6}$
  $- \frac{2}{3}$

11. $\frac{1}{16}$
  $+ \frac{7}{8}$

12. $\frac{3}{10}$
  $+ \frac{2}{5}$

13. $\frac{1}{6}$
  $- \frac{1}{9}$

14. $\frac{4}{7}$
  $+ \frac{1}{4}$

15. $\frac{9}{10}$
  $+ \frac{5}{8}$

16. $\frac{7}{15}$
  $- \frac{1}{5}$

THINK ABOUT IT!

17. Estimate each comparison. Use <, >, or =.

a. $\frac{9}{10} - \frac{4}{9} \bigcirc 1\frac{1}{5} - \frac{4}{5}$

b. $\frac{53}{100} \bigcirc \frac{6}{11} + \frac{7}{13}$

Fractions: More Subtracting

Name _____

Subtract. Write all answers in lowest form.

$$6\frac{1}{8} = 5\frac{9}{8}$$
$$-4\frac{3}{8} = 4\frac{3}{8}$$
$$\overline{1\frac{6}{8}} = 1\frac{3}{4}$$

1. Subtract the fractions first. Rename if necessary.

2. Subtract the whole numbers.

3. Reduce if necessary.

---

1. $12\frac{1}{5}$
   $-\ 3\frac{4}{5}$
   _____

2. $4\frac{2}{7}$
   $-\ 1\frac{3}{7}$
   _____

3. $8\frac{1}{4}$
   $-6\frac{3}{4}$
   _____

4. $7\frac{1}{6}$
   $-\ 4\frac{5}{6}$
   _____

5. $6\frac{7}{16}$
   $-\ 3\frac{9}{16}$
   _____

6. $3\frac{2}{5}$
   $-\ 2\frac{4}{5}$
   _____

7. $8\frac{5}{12}$
   $-\ 2\frac{7}{12}$
   _____

8. $9\frac{2}{10}$
   $-\ 3\frac{7}{10}$
   _____

9. $11\frac{3}{20}$
   $-\ 9\frac{5}{20}$
   _____

10. 34
    $-\ 7\frac{1}{2}$
    _____

11. 26
    $-\ 18\frac{2}{3}$
    _____

12. 16
    $-\ 9\frac{3}{4}$
    _____

13. $10\frac{1}{4}$
    $-\ 7\frac{3}{4}$
    _____

14. $4\frac{5}{12}$
    $-\ 3\frac{7}{12}$
    _____

15. $14\frac{1}{6}$
    $-\ 12\frac{5}{6}$
    _____

16. $9\frac{13}{20}$
    $-\ 6\frac{17}{20}$
    _____

Fractions: Multiplying Fractions

Multiply. Write the product in lowest terms.

$$\frac{2}{3} \times \frac{3}{4} = \frac{6}{12} = \frac{1}{2}$$

1. Multiply the numerators
2. Multiply the denominators.
3. Reduce.

1. $\frac{5}{6} \times \frac{1}{4}$

2. $\frac{1}{9} \times \frac{1}{9}$

3. $\frac{2}{3} \times \frac{1}{3}$

4. $\frac{3}{8} \times \frac{2}{5}$

5. $\frac{5}{6} \times \frac{1}{6}$

6. $\frac{1}{4} \times \frac{1}{8}$

7. $\frac{7}{8} \times \frac{5}{6}$

8. $\frac{2}{4} \times \frac{2}{5}$

9. $\frac{1}{2} \times \frac{3}{6}$

10. $\frac{2}{3} \times \frac{11}{12}$

11. $\frac{5}{8} \times \frac{3}{4}$

12. $\frac{5}{7} \times \frac{4}{9}$

13. $\frac{5}{9} \times \frac{2}{3}$

14. $\frac{1}{2} \times \frac{3}{5}$

15. $\frac{3}{4} \times \frac{3}{4}$

16. $\frac{3}{5} \times \frac{8}{9}$

17. $\frac{3}{5} \times \frac{2}{4}$

18. $\frac{1}{8} \times \frac{5}{6}$

19. $\frac{6}{7} \times \frac{1}{4}$

20. $\frac{1}{6} \times \frac{5}{8}$

 THINK ABOUT IT!

21. Find each missing fraction.

   a. ___ $\times \frac{1}{3} = \frac{2}{9}$

   b. ___ $\times \frac{4}{5} = \frac{16}{25}$

   c. ___ $\times \frac{3}{5} = \frac{1}{5}$

Fractions: Multiplying Mixed Numbers

Multiply. Reduce.

$1\frac{3}{4} \times 8 =$

$\frac{7}{4} \times \frac{8}{1} = \frac{56}{4} = 14$

1. Change each mixed number to an improper fraction.
2. Multiply the numerators.
3. Multiply the denominators.
4. Reduce if possible.

1. $3\frac{1}{4} \times 2\frac{1}{2}$

2. $4\frac{3}{4} \times 2\frac{2}{3}$

3. $2\frac{1}{6} \times 5\frac{2}{5}$

4. $1\frac{2}{3} \times 6$

5. $4\frac{3}{5} \times 5\frac{2}{3}$

6. $6\frac{4}{5} \times 3\frac{3}{4}$

7. $10 \times \frac{5}{12}$

8. $6 \times 3\frac{5}{8}$

9. $3\frac{6}{15} \times 2\frac{3}{4}$

10. $4\frac{1}{10} \times 1\frac{3}{4}$

11. $4\frac{5}{6} \times 3\frac{3}{4}$

12. $3\frac{1}{3} \times 1\frac{9}{10}$

13. $5\frac{4}{9} \times 9\frac{3}{8}$

14. $10\frac{3}{4} \times 3\frac{1}{3}$

15. $4\frac{1}{2} \times 1\frac{3}{4}$

16. $5\frac{2}{3} \times 8\frac{1}{2}$

17. $10 \times \frac{7}{8}$

18. $3\frac{1}{10} \times 12$

19. $1\frac{6}{7} \times 2\frac{1}{4}$

20. $5\frac{2}{3} \times 10\frac{1}{2}$

 ## THINK ABOUT IT!

21. Find each product.

   a. $\frac{3}{5} \times \frac{5}{3}$

   b. $6 \times \frac{1}{6}$

   c. $\frac{4}{7} \times \frac{7}{4}$

22. What pattern do you notice in each of the products above?

Fractions: Problem Solving

Name _____

Solve each problem.

1. Brittany had 60 minutes to take her history test. She spent 10 minutes on the true/false questions, 15 minutes on the short answers, and 20 minutes on the essay. What fraction of the time was left to check her work?

2. Of the 50 US states, 4 have names that begin with the letter **A**. What fraction of the states is that? Write your answer in lowest terms.

3. Anne's house is $5\frac{3}{4}$ miles from school. Joe's house is $3\frac{1}{4}$ miles from school. How much closer is Joe's house to school?

4. Jennifer is baking 2 dozen chocolate chip cookies. If the recipe calls for $\frac{3}{4}$ cup of flour per dozen, how much flour will she need to use?

5. Natalie's basketball game lasted $1\frac{1}{2}$ hours. Earlier in the day, she practiced for three quarters of an hour. How much time did she spend playing basketball that day?

6. Dave gave Jerry half of his $16\frac{3}{4}$ ounce steak. How much does Dave's remaining portion weigh?

7. If Dennie walks at a rate of 4 miles per hour, how far can she walk in $2\frac{3}{4}$ hours?

8. Julie and Sarah ordered a large pizza for dinner. There are sixteen slices in the pizza. If Julie ate $\frac{1}{4}$ of pizza, how many pieces did she eat? If Sarah ate three pieces, what fraction of the pizza did she eat?

1.

2.

3.

4.

5.

6.

7.

8.

Measurement: Length in the Customary System   Name _____

Study the chart below to answer the questions.

```
1 foot = 12 inches
1 yard = 3 feet
1 mile = 5,280 feet or 1,760 yards
```

TIP: *When changing from a smaller unit to a larger one (inches to feet), <u>divide</u>.*
When changing from a larger unit to a smaller one (feet to inches), <u>multiply</u>.

Change each measure to inches.

1. 3 ft

2. 4 yd

3. 2 ft 4 in

4. 9 yd

5. 5 yd 1 ft

6. 120 ft

7. 8 yd

8. 10 ft 7 in

Change each measure to feet.

9. 6 yd

10. 2 mi

11. 72 in

12. 3 yd 1 ft

13. 48 in

14. 5 yd 2 ft

15. $1\frac{1}{2}$ mile

16. 96 in

Write each measure as yards and feet.

17. 37 ft

18. 84 in

19. 22 ft

20. 5 ft 24 in

Write each measure as feet and inches.

21. 28 in

22. 45 in

23. $6\frac{1}{4}$ yd

24. 6 yd 30 in

Measurement: Weight in the Customary System   Name _____

Study the chart below to answer the questions.

> 1 pound (lb) = 16 ounces (oz)
> 2,000 pounds = 1 ton (T)

TIP: *When changing from a smaller unit to a larger one (oz to lb), <u>divide</u>. When changing from a larger unit to a smaller one (T to lb), <u>multiply</u>.*

Change each measure to ounces.

1. 3 lb

2. 18 lb

3. 6 lb 9 oz

4. 12 lb

5. 15 lb 2 oz

6. 7 lb 10 oz

7. 21 lb

8. 30 lb

Change each measure to pounds.

9. 2 T

10. 288 oz

11. 9 T

12. 64 oz

13. 400 oz

14. $4\frac{1}{2}$ T

15. 496 oz

16. $6\frac{3}{4}$ T

Write each measure in pounds and ounces.

17. 33 oz

18. 91 oz

19. 116 oz

20. 598 oz

21. 248 oz

22. 474 oz

23. 82 oz

24. 574 oz

25. 354 oz

26. 65 oz

27. 550 oz

28. 192 oz

Measurement: Capacity in the Customary System   Name _____

Study the chart below to answer the questions.

```
1 pint (pt) = 2 cups (c)
1 quart (qt) = 2 pt
       1 qt = 4 c
1 gallon (gal) = 4 qt
```

TIP: *When changing from a smaller unit to a larger one (c to pt), <u>divide</u>. When changing from a larger unit to a smaller one (qt to pt), <u>multiply</u>.*

Change each measure to cups.

1. 2 pt   2. 3 qt   3. 1 gal   4. 6 qt

5. 3 gal   6. 7 pt   7. 10 qt   8. 5 gal

Change each measure to pints.

9. 10 c   10. 1 gal 3 qt   11. 8 qt   12. 3 gal

13. 6 qt 1 pt   14. 6 c   15. 5 gal 1 qt   16. 12 qt

Change each measure to quarts.

17. 16 pt   18. 6 gal   19. 8 c   20. 4 gal

21. 4 gal 3 qt   22. 10 pt   23. 24 c   24. 2 gal 1 qt

Write each measure in quarts and pints.

25. 9 pt   26. 34 c   27. 25 pt   28. 2 gal 2 c

Measurement: Problem Solving

Name _____

Solve each problem.

1. Lenox Mall is approximately 3 football fields long. If a football field is 100 yards long, how many feet long is the mall?

2. Matt has an extension cord that is 66 inches long. If his driveway is 12 feet long, will the extension cord reach from his house to the end of the driveway?

3. Cheryl is preparing baked potatoes for dinner. She needs to purchase 1½ pounds of potatoes. How many ounces is that?

4. Lanier Middle School's cafeteria prepared 48 turkey sandwiches for Ms. Baker's field trip. If they used 5 oz of turkey per sandwich, how many pounds of turkey did they use?

5. Leigh needs 3 cups of milk, 1 for each of her cats. If she has 1 pint in her refrigerator, does Leigh have enough milk?

6. Jeanette is making tomato soup for dinner. If Jeanette mixes 3 quarts of tomato juice with 2 pints of milk, how many cups of soup will that make?

7. Which is the better buy for one quart of apple juice:
   a. a 1-pint can at $0.90
   b. a 1-quart can at $1.65

8. A box of English grammar textbook weighs approximately 60 pounds. How many ounces is that?

1.

2.

3.

4.

5.

6.

7.

8.

Measurement: Metric System Length   Name _____

Part I: Measure each segment to the nearest centimeter.

1. _____   2. _____

3. _____   4. _____

5. _____   6. _____

Part II: Complete each sentence.

_____ cm = 9 m	*1 centimeter = 10 millimeters*
	1 decimeter (dm) = 10 centimeters
Since 1 m = 100 cm,	*1 meter (m) = 100 centimeters*
9 m = 900 cm.	
	1 kilometer (km) = 1000 meters
<u>900</u> cm = 9 m	*10 decimeters = 1 meter*

7. 7 km = _____ m   8. 16 cm = _____ mm   9. 8 m = _____ cm

10. 11 m = _____ dm   11. 5000 m = _____ km   12. 700 cm = _____ m

13. 40 mm = _____ cm   14. 12 km = _____ m   15. _____ m = 800 cm

16. _____ cm = 17 dm   17. 3.5 m = _____ cm   18. _____ m = 6.8 km

 THINK ABOUT IT!

19. Choose the most sensible measurement.

    a. width of a dollar bill   b. width of a house

      7 cm   7 m   7 km   12 cm   12 dm   12 m

Measurement: Metric System Weight   Name _____

Part I: Would you use grams (g) or kilograms (kg) to measure the following?

A **gram** is a metric unit of weight used to measure the weight of light objects.

A **kilogram** is used to weigh heavy objects.

---

1. bag of oranges

2. piece of paper

3. a clarinet

4. a cat

5. a paper clip

6. bunch of parsley

Part II: Complete each sentence.

> **1 kilogram (kg) = 1000 grams (g)**
>
> *To change kilograms to grams, multiply by 1,000.*
> *To change grams to kilograms, divide by 1,000.*

7.   8 kg = _____ g

8.   2,000 g = _____ kg

9.   11 kg = _____ g

10.   4,500 g = _____ kg

11.   7,000 g = _____ kg

12.   5.5 kg = _____ g

13.   35,000 g = _____ kg

14.   6 kg = _____ g

15.   9,500 g = _____ kg

16.   8.5 kg = _____ g

17.   18,000 g = _____ kg

18.   23 kg = _____ g

 THINK ABOUT IT!

19. If a watermelon is 5 kilograms, and Shelia cuts off a 350-gram slice, how much of the watermelon remains?

Name _____

Measurement: Capacity in the Metric System

Part I: Would you choose milliliters or liters to measure the following?

> A *milliliter* (mL) is a metric unit which is used to measure the capacity of *small objects*.
> A *liter* (L) is a metric unit which is used to measure the capacity of *large objects.*

---

1. coffee in a mug

2. water in a pool

3. gasoline in a tank

4. milk in a glass

5. water in a pond

6. oil in a tablespoon

7. paint in a can

8. a can of soup

9. juice from an orange

Part II: Complete each sentence.

> **1 L = 1,000 mL**
> *To change liters to milliliters, multiply by 1,000.*
> *To change milliliters to liters, divide by 1,000.*

10. 3 L = _____ mL

11. 4,000 mL = _____ L

12. 8,000 mL = _____ L

13. 5.5 L = _____ mL

14. 8.1 L = _____ mL

15. 6,500 mL = _____ L

16. 1,500 mL = ____ L

17. 7 L = _____ mL

18. 5.2 L = _____ mL

 THINK ABOUT IT!

19. Choose *milliliters* or *liters* to complete each sentence.
    a. The cat drank about 6 _____ of milk.
    b. A small pond holds about 180,000 _____ of water.
    c. The jug holds about 750 _____ of juice.

Measurement: Problem Solving

Solve each problem.

1. Ray is 180 cm tall. How many meters is that? How many millimeters?

   1. _____

2. Sarah's father is on the road a great deal traveling for business. If he travels 1,500 km each month, how many kilometers is that every year?

   2. _____

3. Order the following lengths from shortest to longest:
   6 m,   600 mm,   6 cm

   3. _____

4. Together 4 bananas weigh approximately 1 kg. About how many grams is each banana?

   4. _____

5. Julie stepped on the scale and saw that she weighed 31 kg. How many grams does she weigh?

   5. _____

6. Mrs. Smith was pouring lemonade into cups. If she has a 1 liter container of lemonade and each cup holds 190 mL, how many cups can she fill?

   6. _____

7. Sally has four 1-liter bottles of soda. Can she fill 12 250 mL glasses?

   7. _____

8. A bunch of white grapes weighs 160 grams. Would 10 bunches of grapes be more or less than 1 kilogram?

   8. _____

9. Adam is a swimmer. At one of his swim meets, he competed in the 100 m free style. If each lap is 25 m, how many laps did he swim?

   9. _____

Ratio and Percent: Ratios

Name_____

A ratio compares two quantities and can be written as follows:

3 circles to 4 squares

$\frac{3}{4}$ or 3:4 or 3 to 4

Write each ratio three different ways.

---

1. 4 balls to 6 bats

2. 10 bicycles to 9 helmets

3. 5 bananas to 7 apples

4. 3 comedies to 4 dramas

5. 5 shirts to 4 sweaters

6. 12 peanuts to 18 raisins

7. 6 oranges to 11 bananas

8. 13 peaches to 15 plums

9. 11 girls to 23 students

10. 12 boys to 23 students

11. 1 teacher to 26 students

12. 3 administrators to 950 students

13. 2 giraffes to 5 gorillas

14. 18 flamingos to 9 parrots

15. 3 tigers to 4 lions

16. 7 monkeys to 8 apes

 THINK ABOUT IT!

17. The ratio of boys to girls in the school orchestra is 22:25.
    a. Are there more boys or more girls in the orchestra?
    b. How many students are in the orchestra?

Ratio and Percent: Equal Ratios

Part I: Determine whether each pair of ratios is equal. Write <u>yes</u> or <u>no</u>.

$$\overset{9}{\underset{no}{\cancel{\frac{3}{4}}}} , \overset{8}{\frac{2}{3}}$$

1. Cross multiply.
2. If the cross products are equal, the ratios are equal.

1. $\frac{9}{10}$, $\frac{8}{9}$

2. $\frac{14}{16}$, $\frac{7}{8}$

3. $\frac{5}{6}$, $\frac{10}{11}$

4. $\frac{4}{5}$, $\frac{12}{15}$

5. $\frac{3}{8}$, $\frac{6}{16}$

6. $\frac{6}{9}$, $\frac{8}{12}$

7. $\frac{6}{5}$, $\frac{7}{6}$

8. $\frac{8}{20}$, $\frac{6}{15}$

9. $\frac{12}{30}$, $\frac{6}{15}$

Part II: Find each equal ratio.

$$\frac{2}{3} = \frac{x}{12}$$
$$\frac{2}{3} = \frac{8}{12}$$

Since $3 \times 4 = 12$, *multiply* 2×4 to find x.

10. $\frac{15}{20} = \frac{x}{40}$

11. $\frac{2}{3} = \frac{x}{9}$

12. $\frac{4}{5} = \frac{x}{15}$

13. $\frac{5}{9} = \frac{x}{27}$

14. $\frac{75}{100} = \frac{x}{4}$

15. $\frac{8}{10} = \frac{x}{20}$

16. $\frac{12}{15} = \frac{x}{30}$

17. $\frac{5}{4} = \frac{x}{12}$

18. $\frac{24}{30} = \frac{x}{15}$

Ratio & Percent: Understanding Percent

Name _____

Part I: Write each ratio as a percent.

$$52:100 = 52\%$$

A **percent** is a special ratio that compares a quantity to 100.

$$\frac{75}{100} = 75\%$$

1. 29:100

2. $\frac{61}{100}$

3. $\frac{8}{100}$

4. 25:100

5. 5 to 100

6. 85:100

7. 97 to 100

8. $\frac{67}{100}$

9. 40 to 100

10. 13:100

11. $\frac{51}{100}$

12. 75:100

Part II: Write each percent as a ratio (use fractions in lowest terms).

13. 50%

14. 30%

15. 25%

16. 20%

17. 73%

18. 64%

19. 15%

20. 40%

21. 60%

22. 33%

23. 75%

24. 10%

25. 63%

26. 95%

27. 70%

28. 86%

 THINK ABOUT IT!

29. A theater reviewer wrote that the lead actress "gave a 110% effort." What do you think the reviewer meant about the actress' performance?

MATH FACTS

Mathematics now helps athletes to do better in sports. Computers use math to help golfers swing harder, swimmers swim faster, baseball pitchers throw faster and to help ice skaters spin and skate like never before.

Ratio & Percent: Percent of a Number   Name _____

Find the percent of each number. Study the two methods below.

Method I
Use Fractions
75% of 60

$\frac{3}{4} \times 60$

$\boxed{45}$

Method II
Use decimals
51% of 80

$.51 \times 80$

$\boxed{40.8}$

---

1. 50% of 24

2. 10% of 20

3. 25% of 24

4. 6% of 60

5. 40% of 50

6. 5% of 60

7. 20% of 25

8. 24% of 30

9. 15% of 20

10. 35% of 70

11. 50% of 36

12. 30% of 90

13. 10% of 80

14. 40% of 26

15. 4% of 50

16. 40% of 100

17. 25% of 62

18. 90% of 30

19. 10% of 150

20. 50% of 88

21. 33% of 200

 THINK ABOUT IT!

22. Write <, >, or =.

a. 100% of 55 ◯ 55   b. 85% of 55 ◯ 55   c. 125% of 55 ◯ 55

Probability & Statistics: Outcomes   Name _____

Use the information given to solve each problem.

> ### Sarah has 6 chips in a bag, one red, three blue, and two green.

1. How many outcomes are possible is she chooses one chip from the bag?

2. What are the possible outcomes?

3. What is the chance of choosing a *red* chip from the bag? a *green* one?

> ### Tommy is using different colored paper for an art project. He has 5 red, 3 blue, 4 green, 3 yellow, and 6 black pieces of paper.

4. If he chooses one color to start with, what are the possible outcomes?

5. Would he be more likely to select a *red* sheet or *black* one?

6. Which outcomes are equally likely?

> ### Suppose Ray has a twelve-sided die with the numbers 1-12 on twelve sides.

7. If Ray throws the die, list all the possible outcomes.

8. What is the chance of throwing a *three*?

9. Is he more likely to throw a *six* or *twelve*?

Probability & Statistics: Finding Probabilities

Write the probability of each outcome.

> *A **probability** is the chance of something happening.*

1. There are 28 students in Mimi's class. Nine wear glasses, six wear contacts, and the rest of the students need no visual help. What is the probability that someone in her class wears glasses or contacts?

2. When Chris arrives home from work, he empties his change into a small bowl. There are four quarters, five dimes, three nickels, and seven pennies. When Chris reaches for a coin, what is the probability he will choose a dime from the bowl?

3. Jimmy tosses a two-sided coin (heads & tails) in the air. What is the probability it will land on tails?

4. Mrs. Lewis has a plate of cookies for dessert. There are twelve chocolate chip cookies, six oatmeal raisin, and nine sugar cookies. What is the

    a. probability of choosing a sugar cookie?

    b. not choosing an oatmeal raisin?

    c. choosing a sugar or oatmeal raisin cookie?

5. Philip has a collection of football cards. He has 49 cards from the AFC players and 54 from the NFC players. What is the probability of choosing a card from the AFC?

Probability & Statistics: Finding Averages

Find each average. Round to the nearest tenth.

9, 11, 7, 8

9 + 11 + 7 + 8 = 35

1. *Add the numbers.*
2. *Divide by the number of addends.*

35 ÷ 4 = 8.8

---

1. 8, 9, 10

2. 5, 5, 7, 3

3. 5, 4, 9, 10

4. 3, 3, 12, 4, 6

5. 7, 9, 5, 12

6. 4, 9, 13, 5, 11

7. 6, 8, 7, 7, 8

8. 12, 3, 9, 8

9. 9, 11, 8, 12

10. 8, 12, 11, 10

11. 15, 9, 12, 10, 11

12. 7, 6, 9, 7, 8

13. 275, 350, 421

14. 78, 109, 101, 111

15. 65, 99, 87, 67

16. 123, 72, 209

17. 65, 78, 93, 81

18. 67, 87, 103, 99

 THINK ABOUT IT!

19. Is it possible for the average of a group of numbers to be greater than the largest number? Smaller than the smallest number? Explain your answers.

Probability & Statistics: Graphs   Name _____

Use the graphs to answer each question.

Sports Preferences in Paul's Class

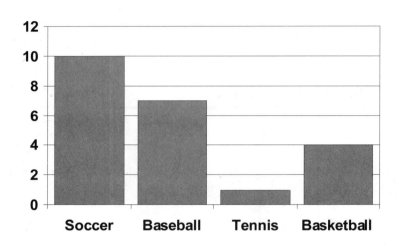

1. How many students favored
   soccer? _____ baseball? _____ tennis? _____ basketball? _____
2. Which sport was favored most? _____
3. Which sport was favored least? _____
4. How many more kids preferred baseball than basketball? _____

Beanie Babies Sold

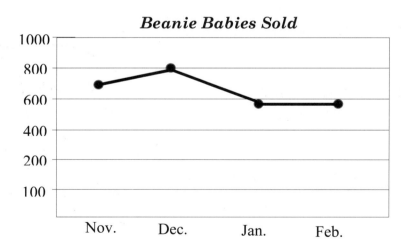

5. In which month were the most Beanie Babies sold? _____
6. In which months were 600 Beanie Babies sold? _____
7. How many Beanie Babies were sold in all four months? _____
8. How many more Beanie Babies were sold in November and December than in
   January and February?

Probability & Statistics: Circle Graphs   Name _____

Use each circle graph to answer the questions. If there is not enough information given, write not enough information.

1. Which hobby is most popular?

2. What percentage of kids were interested in video games?

3. How many students were surveyed for this graph?

4. Write a title for this circle graph.

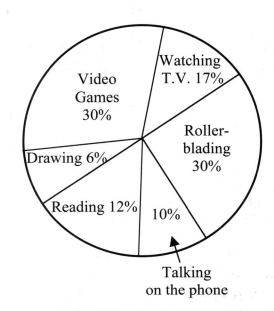

5. How many roses were sold?

6. Which flower was the best seller for the nursery?

7. How many more tulips sold than snapdragons?

8. How many flowers were sold?

9. What percent of flowers sold were azaleas?

10. What percent of flowers sold where daffodils and tulips?

Spring Flowers Sold at the Nursery

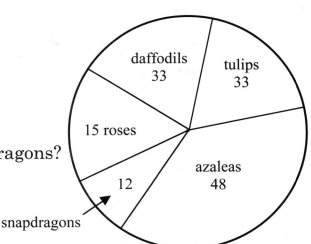

Answer Key

Page 5 1. C, 2. C, 3. A, 4. C, 5. A, 6. B, 7. C, 8. B, 9. A, 10. C, 11. B, 12. C, 13. C, 14. D, 15. A, 16. A

Page 6 17. B, 18. C, 19. A, 20. C, 21. D, 22. C, 23. B, 24. D, 25. C, 26. C

Page 7 27. B, 28. C, 29. D, 30. C, 31. B, 32. B, 33. D, 34. C, 35. C, 36. D, 37. B

Page 8 38. C, 39. D, 40. B, 41. D, 42. B, 43. C, 44. B, 45. A, 46. B, 47. B, 48. B, 49. A, 50. B

Page 9 1. 40, 2. 700, 3. 2,000, 4. 5, 5. 800,000, 6. 70,000,000, 7. 9,000, 8. 600,000, 9. 7,000,000, 10. 300, 11. 40,000,000, 12. 20,000, 13. 30, 14. 900,000,000, 15. 1,000,000 16. Sample Answer: 125,678,125,055 and 135,678,125,055

Page10 1. 8,560, 2. 53,024, 3. 9,064,701, 4. 16,000,894, 5. 36,275, 6. 506,003,200, 7. 17,056,341,018, 8. 28,561,122, 9. 70,816,421,006, 10. 413,737,000,016, 11. 915,361,824,197, 12. 5,008,067, 13. 28,602,143, 14. 41,362,001,066, 15. 100,589,734

Page 11 1. C, 2. B, 3. A, 4. C, 5. B, 6. B, 7. C

Page 12 1. B, 2. C, 3. B, 4. D, 5. D, 6. C, 7. B, 8. B, 9. D, 10. C, 11. A, 12. C

Page 13 1. B, 2. A, 3. D, 4. C, 5. B, 6. A, 7. D, 8. B, 9. B, 10. C, 11. B, 12. B, 13. C, 14. C, 15. B, 16. C

Page 14 1. 902,501, 2. 9,725, 3. 43,560 Sq. Ft., 4. three hundred eighty-four, 5. 1,368 miles, 6. 11,362 stamps, 7. 82,220 cans.

Page 15 1. 12, 2. 23, 3. 42, 4. 26, 5. 47, 6. 49, 7. 20, 8. 34, 9. 73, 10. 39, 11. 38, 12. 43, 13. 80, 14. 76, 15. 48, 16. 54, 17. 43, 18. 42, 19. 40, 20. 64, 21. 65, 22. 100, 23. 75, 24. 82, 25. 100, 26. 58, 27. 56, 28. 156, 29. 90, 30. 63, 31. 99, 32. 54, 33. 71, 34. 44, 35. 48, 36. 60

Page 16 1. 55, 2. 643, 3. 483, 4. 339, 5. 835, 6. 643, 7. 861, 8. 960, 9. 680, 10. 945, 11. 1,061,

12. 2,416, 13. 7,506, 14. 6,620, 15. 5,583, 16. 9,155, 17. 16,674, 18. 28,444, 19. 35,515, 20. 432,248, 21. 577,526, 22. 761,108, 23. 2,497,536, 24. 7,815,519, 25. 235,517,567, 26. 8,655,483, 27. 4,107,526, 28. 10,787,067

Page 17 1. <, 2. <, 3. <, 4. <, 5. >, 6. <, 7. > 8. <, 9. <, 10. >, 11. =, 12. >, 13. >, 14. <, 15. >, 16. <, 17. =, 18. <, 19. >, 20. <

Page 18 1. 50, 2. 90, 3. 80, 4. 50, 5. 400, 6. 900, 7. 7,000, 8. 30,000, 9. 900,000, 10. 300,000, 11. 700,000, 12. 6,000,000, 13. 160, 14. 90, 15. 160, 16. 100, 17. 300, 18. 1,300, 19. 1,000, 20. 6,000, 21. 130,000, 22. 150,000, 23. 4,000,000, 24. 12,000,000

Page 19 1. 110 miles, 2. 753 items, 3. 817 frames
4. 910 tickets, 5. 1,567 strawberries, 6. 70 points

Page 20 1. 5, 2. 7, 3. 12, 4. 4, 5. 9, 6. 6, 7. 8, 8. 13, 9. 11, 10. 8, 11. 13, 12. 11, 13. 19, 14. 18, 15. 19, 16. 43, 17. 48, 18. 51, 19. 38, 20. 65, 21. 129, 22. 111, 23. 254, 24. 105, 25. 336, 26. 272, 27. 1307, 28. 2075, 29. 5858, 30. 4921, 31. 2344, 32. 2307, 33. 8200, 34. 21728, 35. 31856, 36. 35481, 37. 17367, 38. 123516, 39. 121921, 40. 101097, 41. 1542008, 42. 3064178

Page 21 1. 13, 2. 28, 3. 163, 4. 32, 5. 225, 6. 4706, 7. 164, 8. 341, 9. 8359, 10. 1125, 11. 3244, 12. 2409, 13. 7414, 14. 5316, 15. 15031, 16. 11537, 17. 34305, 18. 41406, 19. 34737, 20. 16058, 21. 15672, 22. 114779, 23. 20504, 24. 30562, 25. 30001, 26. 41738, 27. 124739, 28. 1712676

Page 22 1. 100, 2. 700, 3. 400, 4. 400, 5. 400, 6. 1000, 7. 3000, 8. 7000, 9. 7000, 10. 9000, 11. 7000, 12. 8000, 13. 0, 14. 100, 15. 200, 16. 0, 17. 300, 18. 400, 19. 200, 20. 300, 21. 4000, 22. 2000, 23. 1000, 24. 6000, 25. 10000, 26. 10000, 27. 10000, 28. 10000

Page 23 1. 22 students, 2. 3 games, 3. 44 bracelets, 4. 385 pages, 5. 159 rolls, 6. 2,306 miles, 7. 13,730 feet

Page 24 1. 48, 2. 66, 3. 72, 4. 120, 5. 45, 6. 24, 7. 72, 8. 121, 9. 77, 10. 99, 11. 110, 12. 84, 13. 50, 14. 96, 15. 42, 16. 80, 17. 81, 18. 108, 19. 88, 20. 20, 21. 35, 22. 144, 23. 100, 24. 132, 25. 8, 26. 12, 27. 10, 28. 9, 29. 5, 30. 10, 31. 7, 32. 7, 33. 7, 34. 8, 35. 4, 36. 3, 37. 6, 38. 3, 39. 3, 40. 10, 41. 7, 42. 9, 43. 4, 44. 6, 45. 4

Page 25 1. 216, 2. 160, 3. 240, 4. 336, 5. 294, 6. 225, 7. 512, 8. 960, 9. 1512, 10. 336, 11. 60, 12. 64, 13. 42, 14. 25, 15. 49, 16. 81, 17. 100, 18. 66, 19. 80, 20. 192

Page 26 1. 112, 2. 180, 3. 468, 4. 644, 5. 441, 6. 528, 7. 360, 8. 152, 9. 602, 10. 480, 11. 648, 12. 891, 13. 805, 14. 690, 15. 756, 16. 2632, 17. 1712, 18. 6272, 19. 4473, 20. 1178, 21. 3940, 22. 1746, 23. 4602, 24. 4470, 25. 6356, 26. 6183, 27. 6384, 28. 5082

Page 27 1. 2556, 2. 7824, 3. 6300, 4. 4272, 5. 6613, 6. 16226, 7. 20930, 8. 14526, 9. 11875, 10. 21868, 11. 14399, 12. 35010, 13. 4650, 14. 7584, 15. 11115, 16. 34048, 17. 12648, 18. 48546, 19. 43380, 20. 63115

Page 28 1. 8656, 2. 25972, 3. 36155, 4. 28704, 5. 56240, 6. 72285, 7. 107768, 8. 179232, 9. 337732, 10. 1053585, 11. 3645282, 12. 5080411, 13. 1104696, 14. 1423580, 15. 2848272, 16. 845328, 17. 2021417, 18. 2745728, 19. 5538780, 20. 6888864

Page 29 1. 368, 2. 675, 3. 522, 4. 380, 5. 412, 6. 635, 7. 1113, 8. 1488, 9. 3948, 10. 2322, 11. 1395, 12. 1408, 13. 1390, 14. 1304, 15. 3344, 16. 3724, 17. 13015, 18. 17043, 19. 34686, 20. 63440, 21. 19208, 22. 46094, 23. 92976, 24. 197610, 25. 2288 pages

Page 30 1. 40755, 2. 49760, 3. 94560, 4. 34600, 5. 61349, 6. 77859, 7. 95988, 8. 150280, 9. 199330, 10. 347400, 11. 304080, 12. 603718, 13. 549956, 14. 310086, 15. 90048, 16. 145827, 17. 2481660, 18. 2981858, 19. 6099078, 20. 4181940, 21. 4371213, 22. 8992494, 23. 16442764, 24. 26991531

Page 31 1. 480, 2. 450, 3. 180, 4. 480, 5. 630, 6. 540, 7. 640, 8. 450, 9. 3200, 10. 2000, 11. 1800,

Page 31 continued
12. 700, 13. 4500, 14. 2000, 15. 6400, 16. 3500, 17. 6000, 18. 5600, 19. 1200, 20. 5600, 21. Because 138 is being rounded down to 100.

Page 32 1. 1200, 2. 2700, 3. 10000, 4. 12000, 5. 12000, 6. 15000, 7. 35000, 8. 56000, 9. 40000, 10. 80000, 11. 120000, 12. 150000, 13. 200000, 14. 240000, 15. 280000, 16. 560000, 17. 900000, 18. 1800000, 19. 1600000, 20. 4000000

Page 33 1. 84 cupcakes, 2. 30 miles, 3. 96 flowers
4. 168 labels, 5. 210 donuts, 6. 473 words, 7. 120 roses, 8. 102 strawberries, 9. A. 540 rolls, B. 585 packages

Pages 34 1. 900 pieces, 2. 720 cranes, 3. 876 candies, 4. 1176 folders, 5. 1920 seeds, 6. 8556 calendars, 7. 2834 miles, 8. 5328 plants

Page 35 1. 11, 2. 12, 3. 10, 4. 12, 5. 7, 6. 6, 7. 12, 8. 12, 9. 9, 10. 7, 11. 3, 12. 12, 13. 12, 14. 11, 15. 7, 16. 9, 17. 9, 18. 0, 19. 10, 20. 12, 21. 5, 22. 5, 23. 5, 24. 12, 25. 9, 26. 5, 27. 8, 28. 3, 29. 6, 30. 5, 31. 10, 32. 3, 33. 8, 34. 42, 35. 10, 36. 30, 37. 10, 38. 49, 39. 10, 40. 7, 41. 110, 42. 12, 43. 6, 44. 90, 45. 11

Page 36 1. 6, 2. 27, 3. 7, 4. 36, 5. 42, 6. 11, 7. 21, 8. 28, 9. 36, 10. 15, 11. 17, 12. 68, 13. 23, 14. 60, 15. 108, 16. 70, 17. 99, 18. 45, 19. 55, 20. 72

Page 37 1. 52 R2, 2. 97 R1, 3. 123 R5, 4. 74 R6, 5. 137 R5, 6. 157 R3, 7. 99 R3, 8. 82 R1, 9. 529 R6, 10. 649 R1, 11. 1277, 12. 960 R2, 13. 826 R2, 14. 997 R6, 15. 1441 R4, 16. 978 R8

Page 38 1. 15 R4, 2. 21 R1, 3. 14 R2, 4. 14 R3, 5. 33, 6. 25 R5, 7. 29 R5, 8. 85 R1, 9. 84 R2, 10. 51 R1, 11. 64 R6, 12. 92 R7, 13. 397, 14. 1339, 15. 821 R2, 16. 944, 17. 951 R1, 18. 979 R3, 19. 994 R6, 20. 969 R2, 21. 533 books

Page 39 1. 9 boards, 2. 16 sets, 3. 19 tables, 4. 34 businesses, 5. 31 groups, 6. 25 boxes, 7. 20 rows, 8. 28 containers, 9. 31 pieces

Page 40 1. 40 friends, 2. 20 pages, 3. 20 days, 4. 53 groups, 5. 124 racks, 6. 25 rows, 7. 75 invitations, 8. 87 packages; 10 brownies, 9. 78 boxes

Page 41 1. 2:30, 2. 7:50, 3. 12:40, 4. 4:50, 5. 10:15, 6. 1:40, 7. 7:40 p.m., 8. 8:30 a.m., 9. 12:40 p.m, 10. 9:55 a.m., 11. 4:00 p.m., 12. 5:20 a.m., 13. 4:30 p.m., 14. 12:00 p.m., 15. 8:40 a.m.

Page 42 1. 10:00 a.m., 2. 10:00 a.m., 3. 9:00 a.m., 4. 3:00 p.m., 5. 1:00 p.m., 6. 10:15 a.m., 7. 1:30 p.m., 8. 7:00 p.m., 9. 8:30 p.m.

Page 43 1. 2 hours, 2. 2 hours, 3. 50 minutes, 4. 5:15 p.m., 5. 5:00 p.m., 6. 1 ½ hours, 7. 7:10 p.m., 8. 12:30 p.m., 9. 10:15 a.m.

Page 44 1. $34.65, 2. $38.10, 3. $66.78, 4. $79.36, 5. $123.84, 6. $231.48, 7. $278.18, 8. $273.84, 9. $527.52, 10. $516.78, 11. $394.20, 12. $680.45, 13. $1,094.16, 14. $1,970.46, 15. $1,529.88, 16. $2,921.92, 17. $3,027.22, 18. $2,821.50, 19. $6,073.74, 20. $9,704.32, 21. $4,912.32, 22. $15,617.25, 23. $9,704.03, 24. $27,988.64, 25. $65.85

Page 45 1. $2.03, 2. $2.52, 3. $3.81, 4. $3.26, 5. $5.28, 6. $4.95, 7. $5.28, 8. $8.11, 9. $5.56, 10. $10.08, 11. $8.23, 12. $8.65, 13. $24.55, 14. $17.01, 15. $12.41, 16. $17.65, 17. $32.37, 18. $59.88, 19. $93.23, 20. $165.79

Page 46 1. $53.49, 2. $224.25, 3. $682.20, 4. $578.25, 5. $1,148.80, 6. $114.45, 7. $2,750, 8. $51.66, 9. $10.80

Page 47 1. $\overrightarrow{UV}$, 2. Point Q, 3. $\overline{LM}$, 4. Point T, 5. $\overleftrightarrow{ST}$, 6. $\overrightarrow{KJ}$, 7. A B, 8. A B, 9. ● E, 10. X Y, 11. N O, 12. R S, 13. a. 2, b. 1, c. none

Page 48 1. yes; hexagon, 2. yes; octagon, 3. yes; rectangle, 4. no, 5. yes; triangle, 6. no, 7. yes; rhombus, 8. yes; pentagon, 9. no, 10. a. squares, b. triangles, rectangles

Page 49 1. acute, 2. obtuse, 3. right, 4. acute, 5. acute, 6. obtuse, 7. right, 8. obtuse, 9. obtuse, 10. acute, 11. right, 12. right, 13. 89°; 179°

Page 50 1. isosceles; acute, 2. scalene; obtuse, 3. scalene; right, 4. equilateral; obtuse, 5. isosceles;

Page 50 continued
5. acute, 6. isosceles; right, 7. a. never, b. always, c. sometimes

Page 51 1. Z, 2. $\overline{ZW}$, $\overline{ZV}$, $\overline{ZU}$, $\overline{ZY}$, $\overline{ZX}$, 3. $\overline{VY}$, $\overline{WU}$, 4. $\overline{VU}$, 5. angle VZW, angle VZU, angle WZX, angle WZY, angle XZY, angle XZU, angle YZU, angle VZX, 6. angle UVZ or angle ZUV, 7. it is half, 8. a. no, b. yes, c. yes, d. yes

Page 52 1. 27 in, 2. 36 ft, 3. 20 cm, 4. 27 m, 5. 80 ft, 6. 90 m, 7. the first room (17 ft x 16 ft)

Page 53 1. 49 m^2, 2. 40 m^2, 3. 99 cm^2, 4. 81 cm^2, 5. 42 m^2, 6. 30 yd^2, 7. 16 ft^2, 8. 32 ft^2, 9. no; it will quadruple

Page 54 1. acute, 2. 91°; 179°, 3. 5 ft, 4. no; an isosceles triangle has only 2 sides equal; an equilateral has 3 sides equal, 5. yes; no, 6. 26 ft 6 in, 7. 18 ft, 8. 20 cm

Page 55 1. 0.2, 2. 0.9, 3. 0.07, 4. 0.12, 5. 10.2, 6. 0.009, 7. 0.25, 8. 5.041, 9. 5.04, 10. 3.003, 11. 31.1, 12. 400.005, 13. 8 hundredths, 14. 8 thousandths, 15. two and fifty-two thousandths, 16. ten and eleven hundredths, 17. three hundred twenty-five thousandths, 18. three and fifty-two thousandths, 19. twenty-five hundredths, 20. fifteen thousandths, 21. four and one hundred ninety-seven thousandths, 22. six and fifty-three thousandths, 23. five and fifty-three hundredths, 24. sixteen and thirty-seven thousandths, 25. nine hundred two thousandths, 26. twenty-one and one hundred forty-three thousandths, 27. fifty-three and two hundred eighty-one thousandths

Page 56 1. >, 2. <, 3. >, 4. <, 5. =, 6. <, 7. >, 8. <, 9. 0.1, 0.3, 0.5, 10. 3.5, 3.7, 3.8, 11. 4.052, 4.5, 4.52, 12. 0.006, 0.06, 0.6, 13. 0.05, 0.5, 2.05, 2.5, 14. 0.62, 0.612, 0.621, 0.625, 15. Sample Answers: a. 0.3, b. 15.45, c. 0.065

Page 57 1. 4, 2. 8.5, 3. 6, 4. 0.6, 5. 10.1, 6. 4, 7. 4.37, 8. 9.95, 9. 6.53, 10. 8, 11. 8.82, 12. 0.36, 13. 10, 14. 10, 15. 9, 16. 22, 17. 4, 18. 35, 19. 3, 20. 30

Page 58 1. 1, 2. 6.08, 3. 5.81, 4. 11.73, 5. 38.21, 6. 38.8, 7. 8.6, 8. 13.48, 9. 1.22, 10. 50.6, 11. 0.55, 12.

Page 58 continued
8.894, 13. 23.8, 14. 19.31, 15. 6.45, 16. 340.6, 17. 81.03, 18. 34.75, 19. 8.088, 20. 22.82, 21. 69.676, 22. $45.90

Page 59 1. 0.3, 2. 6.32, 3. 5.03, 4. 1.29, 5. 0.73, 6. 13.65, 7. 5.57, 8. 2.3, 9. 0.05, 10. 25.08, 11. 0.17, 12. 4.358, 13. 2.8, 14. 1.26, 15. 0.29, 16. 7.2, 17. 61.37, 18. 2.93, 19. 2.959, 20. 8.48, 21. 58.324, 22. $17.25

Page 60 1. 3.2, 2. 0.35, 3. 2.73, 4. 2.853, 5. 17.78, 6. 0.0384, 7. 2.002, 8. 18.56, 9. 4.1535, 10. .0902, 11. 0.03292, 12. 174.24, 13. 159.1, 14. 15.91, 15. 1.591, 16. 0.1591, 17. 0.0012, 18. 0.306, 19. 0.0075
20. 0.252

Page 61 1. 4.2, 2. 11.23, 3. 6.23, 4. 0.861, 5. 4.19, 6. 4.62, 7. 5.1, 8. 2.4, 9. 3.4, 10. 137.36, 11. 17.96, 12. 67.77, 13. 34.5, 14. 0.084, 15. 815.6, 16. 0.788

Page 62 1. 51; 5, 2. 5.62 or 5.63 or 5.64, 3. $4.00
4. $4.18, 5. $1.05, 6. $27.24, 7. $50, 8. 7

Page 63 1. $\frac{1}{3}$, 2. $\frac{1}{2}$, 3. $\frac{3}{4}$, 4. $\frac{1}{5}$, 5. $\frac{2}{3}$, 6. $\frac{4}{5}$, 7. $\frac{2}{5}$, 8. $\frac{9}{14}$, 9. $\frac{4}{7}$, 10. $\frac{3}{8}$, 11. $\frac{8}{15}$, 12. $\frac{2}{3}$, 13. $\frac{1}{2}$, 14. $\frac{2}{3}$, 15. $\frac{3}{10}$, 16. $\frac{1}{2}$, 17. $\frac{5}{6}$, 18. $\frac{4}{7}$, 19. $\frac{3}{5}$, 20. $\frac{12}{25}$, 21. $\frac{3}{8}$, 22. $\frac{62}{75}$, 23. $\frac{3}{4}$, 24. $\frac{3}{8}$, 25. No. If they are both even, they can be reduced by dividing by 2.

Page 64 1. .5, 2. .15, 3. .4, 4. .6, 5. .25, 6. .7, 7. .6, 8. .08, 9. .2, 10. .8, 11. .3, 12. .2, 13. .36, 14. .9, 15. .17, 16. .75, 17. $\frac{3}{10}$, 18. $\frac{9}{10}$, 19. $\frac{7}{10}$, 20. $\frac{1}{10}$, 21. $\frac{11}{25}$, 22. $\frac{14}{25}$, 23. $1\frac{8}{25}$, 24. $2\frac{53}{100}$, 25. $12\frac{3}{5}$, 26. $4\frac{3}{20}$, 27. $7\frac{1}{20}$, 28. $20\frac{7}{100}$

Page 65 1. $2\frac{2}{5}$, 2. $3\frac{1}{5}$, 3. $8\frac{1}{2}$, 4. $4\frac{2}{7}$, 5. $5\frac{1}{3}$, 6. $3\frac{1}{4}$, 7. 20, 8. $7\frac{1}{4}$, 9. $4\frac{1}{6}$, 10. 10, 11. $2\frac{1}{2}$, 12. $12\frac{1}{4}$, 13. $6\frac{1}{3}$, 14. $3\frac{1}{3}$, 15. 4, 16. $\frac{11}{4}$, 17. $\frac{14}{3}$, 18. $\frac{17}{5}$, 19. $\frac{15}{8}$, 20. $\frac{19}{8}$, 21. $\frac{29}{6}$, 22. $\frac{37}{5}$, 23. $\frac{7}{4}$, 24. $\frac{34}{4}$, 25. $\frac{46}{7}$, 26. $\frac{26}{5}$, 27. $\frac{61}{9}$, 28. $\frac{9}{2}$, 29. $\frac{37}{7}$, 30. $\frac{31}{4}$

Page 66 1. $\frac{6}{15}$, $\frac{5}{15}$, 2. $\frac{6}{8}$, $\frac{3}{8}$, 3. $\frac{3}{6}$, $\frac{1}{6}$ 4. $\frac{5}{20}$, $\frac{14}{20}$, 5. $\frac{5}{6}$, $\frac{4}{6}$, 6. $\frac{3}{4}$, $\frac{2}{4}$, 7. $\frac{15}{20}$, $\frac{8}{20}$, 8. $\frac{4}{18}$, $\frac{3}{18}$, 9. $\frac{4}{12}$, $\frac{9}{12}$, 10. $\frac{21}{35}$, $\frac{15}{35}$, 11. $\frac{16}{36}$, $\frac{33}{36}$, 12. $\frac{21}{24}$, $\frac{22}{24}$, 13. $\frac{12}{16}$, $\frac{9}{16}$, 14. $\frac{48}{60}$, $\frac{55}{60}$, 15. $\frac{7}{15}$, $\frac{9}{15}$, 16. $\frac{6}{12}$, $\frac{10}{12}$, $\frac{9}{12}$, 17. $\frac{16}{24}$, $\frac{9}{24}$, $\frac{6}{24}$, 18. $\frac{18}{60}$, $\frac{35}{60}$, $\frac{44}{60}$, 19. Because it might save you from reducing.

Page 67 1. $\frac{5}{7}$, 2. $\frac{3}{5}$, 3. $\frac{1}{2}$, 4. $\frac{1}{2}$, 5. $\frac{1}{2}$, 6. $\frac{1}{3}$, 7. 1, 8. $\frac{1}{3}$, 9. $\frac{1}{5}$, 10. 1, 11. $\frac{5}{8}$, 12. $\frac{1}{3}$, 13. $9\frac{2}{3}$, 14. 5, 15. $22\frac{3}{4}$, 16. $1\frac{1}{5}$

Page 68 1. $\frac{1}{3}$, 2. $\frac{23}{24}$, 3. $\frac{4}{35}$, 4. $1\frac{5}{8}$, 5. $\frac{17}{30}$, 6. $1\frac{1}{15}$, 7. $\frac{7}{36}$, 8. $1\frac{1}{12}$, 9. $1\frac{3}{8}$, 10. $\frac{1}{6}$, 11. $\frac{15}{16}$, 12. $\frac{7}{10}$, 13. $\frac{1}{18}$, 14. $\frac{23}{28}$, 15. $1\frac{21}{40}$, 16. $\frac{4}{15}$, 17. a. >, b. <

Page 69 1. $8\frac{2}{5}$, 2. $2\frac{6}{7}$, 3. $1\frac{1}{2}$, 4. $2\frac{1}{3}$, 5. $2\frac{7}{8}$, 6. $\frac{3}{5}$, 7. $5\frac{5}{6}$, 8. $5\frac{1}{2}$, 9. $1\frac{9}{10}$, 10. $26\frac{1}{2}$, 11. $7\frac{1}{3}$, 12. $6\frac{1}{4}$, 13. $2\frac{1}{2}$, 14. $\frac{5}{6}$, 15. $1\frac{1}{3}$, 16. $2\frac{4}{5}$

Page 70 1. $\frac{5}{24}$, 2. $\frac{1}{81}$, 3. $\frac{2}{9}$, 4. $\frac{3}{20}$, 5. $\frac{5}{36}$, 6. $\frac{1}{32}$,
7. $\frac{35}{48}$, 8. $\frac{1}{5}$, 9. $\frac{1}{4}$, 10. $\frac{11}{18}$, 11. $\frac{15}{32}$, 12. $\frac{20}{63}$, 13. $\frac{10}{27}$, 14. $\frac{3}{10}$, 15. $\frac{9}{16}$, 16. $\frac{8}{15}$, 17. $\frac{3}{10}$, 18. $\frac{5}{48}$, 19. $\frac{3}{14}$, 20. $\frac{5}{48}$, 21. a. $\frac{2}{3}$, b. $\frac{4}{5}$, c. $\frac{5}{15}$

Page 71 1. $8\frac{1}{8}$, 2. $12\frac{2}{3}$, 3. $11\frac{7}{10}$, 4. 10, 5. $26\frac{1}{15}$, 6. $25\frac{1}{2}$, 7. $4\frac{1}{6}$, 8. $21\frac{3}{4}$, 9. $9\frac{7}{20}$, 10. $7\frac{7}{40}$, 11. $18\frac{1}{8}$, 12. $6\frac{1}{3}$, 13. $51\frac{1}{24}$, 14. $35\frac{5}{6}$, 15. $7\frac{7}{8}$, 16. $48\frac{1}{6}$, 17. $8\frac{3}{4}$, 18. $37\frac{1}{5}$, 19. $4\frac{5}{28}$, 20. $59\frac{1}{2}$, 21. a. 1 b. 1, c. 1, 22. All fractions are reciprocals and products are 1.

Page 72 1. $\frac{1}{4}$ of an hour, 2. $\frac{2}{25}$, 3. $2\frac{1}{2}$ miles, 4. $1\frac{1}{2}$ cups, 5. 2¼ hours, 6. $8\frac{3}{8}$ ounces, 7. 11 miles, 8. 4 pieces; $\frac{3}{16}$

Page 73 1. 36 in, 2. 144 in, 3. 28 in, 4. 324 in, 5. 192 in, 6. 1,440 in, 7. 288 in, 8. 127 in, 9. 18 ft, 10. 10,560 ft, 11. 6 ft, 12. 10 ft, 13. 4 ft, 14. 17 ft, 15. 7,920 ft, 16. 8 ft, 17. 12 yd 1 ft, 18. 2 yd 1 ft, 19. 7 yd 1 ft, 20. 2 yd 1 ft, 21. 2 ft 4 in, 22. 3 ft 9 in, 23. 18 ft 9 in, 24. 20 ft 6 in

Page 74 1. 48 oz, 2. 288 oz, 3. 105 oz, 4. 192 oz, 5. 242 oz, 6. 122 oz, 7. 336 oz, 8. 480 oz, 9. 4,000 lb, 10. 18 lb, 11. 18,000 lb, 12. 4 lb, 13. 25 lb, 14. 9,000 lb, 15. 31 lb, 16. 13,500 lb, 17. 2 lb 1oz, 18. 5 lb 11 oz, 19. 7 lb 4 oz, 20. 37 lb 6 oz, 21. 15 lb 8 oz, 22. 29 lb 10 oz, 23. 5 lb 2 oz, 24. 35 lb 14 oz, 25. 22 lb 2 oz, 26. 4 lb 1 oz, 27. 34 lb 6 oz, 28. 12 lb

Page 75 1. 4 c, 2. 12 c, 3. 16 c, 14. 24 c, 5. 48 c, 6. 14 c, 7. 40 c, 8. 80 c, 9. 5 pt, 10. 14 pt, 11. 16 pt, 12. 24 pt, 13. 13 pt, 14. 3 pt, 15. 42 pt, 16. 24 pt, 17. 8 qt, 18. 24 qt, 19. 2 qt, 20. 16 qt, 21. 19 qt, 22. 5 qt, 23. 6 qt, 24. 9 qt, 25. 4 qt 1 pt, 26. 8 qt 1 pt, 27. 12 qt 1 pt, 28.8 qt 1 pt

Page 76 1. 300 ft, 2. no, 3. 24 oz, 4. 15 lb, 5. no, 6. 28 c, 7. b, 8. 960 oz

Page 77 1. 1 cm, 2. 6 cm, 3. 3 cm, 4. 2 cm, 5. 4 cm, 6. 4 cm, 7. 7,000, 8. 160, 9. 800, 10. 110, 11. 5, 12. 7, 13. 4, 14. 12,000, 15. 8, 16. 170, 17. 350, 18. 6,800, 19. a. 7 cm, b. 12 m,

Page 78 1. kilograms, 2. grams, 3. kilograms, 4. kilograms, 5. grams, 6. grams, 7. 8,000, 8. 2, 9. 11,000, 10. 4.5, 11. 7, 12. 5,500, 13. 35, 14. 6,000, 15. 9.5, 16. 8,500, 17. 18, 18. 23,000, 19. 4,650 grams

Page 79 1. mL, 2. L, 3. L, 4. mL, 5. L, 6. mL, 7. L, 8. mL, 9. mL, 10. 3,000, 11. 4, 12. 8, 13. 5,500, 14. 8,100, 15. 6.5, 16. 1.5, 17. 7,000, 18. 5,200, 19. a. milliliters, b. liters, c. milliliters

Page 80 1. 1.8 m; 1,800 mm, 2. 18,000 km, 3. 6 cm, 600 mm, 6 m, 4. 250 g, 5. 31,000 g, 6. 5 cups, 7. yes, 8. more, 9. 4 laps

Page 81 1. $\frac{4}{6}$ or 4:6 or 4 to 6, 2. $\frac{10}{9}$ or 10:9 or 10 to 9, 3. $\frac{5}{7}$ or 5:7 or 5 to 7, 4. $\frac{3}{4}$ or 3:4 or 3 to 4, 5. $\frac{5}{4}$ or 5:4 or 5 to 4, 6. $\frac{12}{18}$ or 12:18 or 12 to 18, 7. $\frac{6}{11}$ or 6:11 or 6 to 11, 8. $\frac{13}{15}$ or 13:15 or 13 to 15, 9. $\frac{11}{23}$ or 11:23 or 11 to 23, 10. $\frac{12}{23}$ or 12:23 or 12 to 23, 11. $\frac{1}{26}$ or 1:26 or 1 to 26, 12. $\frac{3}{950}$ or 3:950, 3 to 950, 13. $\frac{2}{5}$ or 2:5 or 2 to 5, 14. $\frac{18}{9}$ or 18:9 or 18 to 9, 15. $\frac{3}{4}$ or 3:4 or 3 to 4, 16. $\frac{7}{8}$ or 7:8 or 7 to 8, 17. a. girls, b. 47

Page 82 1. no, 2. yes, 3. no, 4. yes, 5. yes, 6. yes, 7. no, 8. yes, 9. yes, 10. 30, 11. 6, 12. 12, 13. 15, 14. 3, 15. 16, 16. 24, 17. 15, 18. 12

Page 83 1. 29%, 2. 61%, 3. 80%, 4. 25%, 5. 5%, 6. 85%, 7. 97%, 8. 67%, 9. 40%, 10. 13%, 11. 51%, 12. 75%, 13. $\frac{1}{2}$, 14. $\frac{3}{10}$, 15. $\frac{1}{4}$, 16. $\frac{1}{5}$, 17. $\frac{73}{100}$, 18. $\frac{16}{25}$, 19. $\frac{3}{20}$, 20. $\frac{2}{5}$, 21. $\frac{3}{5}$, 22. $\frac{33}{100}$, 23. $\frac{3}{4}$, 24. $\frac{1}{10}$, 25. $\frac{63}{100}$, 26. $\frac{19}{20}$, 27. $\frac{7}{10}$, 28. $\frac{43}{50}$, 29. She gave a very good performance , more than was expected.

Page 84 1. 12, 2. 2, 3. 6, 4. 3.6, 5. 20, 6. 3, 7. 5, 8. 7.2, 9. 3, 10. 24.5, 11. 18, 12. 27, 13. 8, 14. 10.4, 15. 2, 16. 40, 17. 15.5, 18. 27, 19. 15, 20. 44, 21. 66, 22. a. =, b. <, c. >

Page 85 1. 3, 2. red, blue, or green, 3. $\frac{1}{6}$, $\frac{1}{3}$, 4. red, blue, green, yellow, or black, 5. black, 6. blue and yellow, 7. 1, 2, 3, 4, 5, 6, 7, 8, 9, 10, 11, 12, 8. $\frac{1}{12}$, 9. equally likely to throw both

Page 86 1. $\frac{15}{28}$, 2. $\frac{5}{19}$, 3. $\frac{1}{2}$, 4. a. $\frac{1}{3}$, b. $\frac{7}{9}$, c. $\frac{5}{9}$, 5. $\frac{49}{103}$

Page 87 1. 9, 2. 5, 3. 7, 4. 5.6, 5. 8.3, 6. 8.4, 7. 7.2, 8. 8, 9. 10, 10. 10.3, 11. 11.4, 12. 7.4, 13. 348.7 14. 99.8, 15. 79.5, 16. 134.7, 17. 79.3, 18. 89, 19. No; it must be in between the largest and the smallest.

Page 88 1. 10; 7; 1; 4, 2. soccer, 3. tennis, 4. 3, 5. December, 6. January & February, 7. 2700, 8. 300

Page 89 1. video games and rollerblading tie, 2. 30%, 3. not enough information, 4. Answers will vary: "Kids' Hobbies," 5. 15, 6. azaleas, 7. 21, 8. 141, 9. 34%, 10. 47%